BLACKBURN AND DARWEN
A CENTURY AGO

£3.60

This book is a reprint of part of a book first published in 1889
by The Historical Publishing Company.

The introductory essay is by Alan Duckworth.
The copyright is held by Landy Publishing and Alan Duckworth

Landy Publishing
3 Staining Rise
Staining, Blackpool FY3 0BU
Tel: (0253) 886103

ISBN: 0 9507692 8 2

Printed by Galava Printing Company Limited, Nelson, Lancashire

BLACKBURN AND DARWEN
A CENTURY AGO

with Introduction by
Alan Duckworth

Landy Publishing
1989

Preface

An old book came into the publisher's hands a few years ago. Its title was difficult to place, as it extended to seven lines. It was intended as the first part of a series of books showing the cities and towns of Lancashire - *"The Premier County of the Kingdom"*, giving details of the towns' history, their statistics, and telling of the businesses in the towns. It was similar to another book published around that time (1889) called "The Century's Progress". The original preface referred to the book as "The Industries of Lancashire". It declared its object as *"portraying with all possible clearness the prominent phases of Lancashire's commercial greatness"*, and went on to say that the book would *"better acquaint the business man with his fellows in commerce, and more fully familiarise the buyer with the seller"*. As with all commercial directories, only those firms who paid to be in it were represented, and probably had some say in what was said about them. Despite this, the likelihood is that most businesses were represented in its pages, and the information given is fascinating today to the person interested in the commercial past of Blackburn and Darwen, the two towns selected from within the pages of the book. It can be seen as a "yellow pages" of a century ago.

To give life to the list of businesses, local historian Alan Duckworth has written an essay on life in the twin towns just a hundred years ago. He wishes to acknowledge the help he received in producing this from Stanley Miller, Blackburn historian and librarian.

Introduction

Are you adventurous? If you got the chance to travel to the Blackburn of 1889, would you take it?

Imagine a fine Summer's day. You've just parked your car on the multi-storey and you're waiting for the lift. You step inside, but instead of a button marked "Shops", you find one marked "1889". Would you press it, and what would you find if you did?

Well you wouldn't step out into a concrete and tile shopping mall. You'd be back in the old market hall with its famous clock tower. No doubt the crush of the crowd would be as bad as ever. Folk who slept several to a bed and shared a privy with half the street would not be shy of physical contact. But what would it look like, what would it sound like and feel like?

Luckily we don't have to rely entirely on imagination and guesswork. In the early 1890's a correspondent on the Blackburn Times recorded his impressions of the town and its people in a series of articles. This is how he described the market:

"Here before us are humbugs, butterscotch, treacle lumps, Everton toffee, brown toffee, yellow toffee, white toffee ... potatoes from the Channel Islands, dark green cabbages and cauliflowers, and the early consignment of peas ... cooling salads, radishes, watercress, shallots, lettuces and parsley ..."

"Here are women and girls buying all kinds of remnants and rags, all dirt cheap. The stalls contain the greatest possible assortment of jumbled drapery and goods. Such a medley of ribbons, flowers, tapes, buttons, stuffs, prints ..."

So we've pressed that button and here we are. What strikes us first?

The noise is different. There's plenty of it; clattering clogs; clomping hooves; rattling wheels; the babble of the crowd; the cries of the traders, but there's no piped music; none of that accumulated roar of cars and buses and heavy lorries; no radios; no televisions; no juke boxes.

Then there's the contrast in people's appearance. There are women as bright and gay as butterflies, and there are dusty, drab women with black shawls over their heads; there are men as smart as paint with glossy toppers and jaunty boaters, and there are men in tattered, hard-worn clothing and mis-shapen hats.

Our man at the Blackburn Times sums up the working man as *"fustianed, clogged and unwashed"*, he sees boys in *"baggy, raggy trousers with overgrown jackets,"* and girls in *"rags, dirty almost to filthiness"*.

In contrast the Blackburn Standard describes the latest fashion for the well-to-do:

"The directoire coat is entirely dead ... The most stylish thing for evening wear is a low bodice with long sleeves: the former edged with a fall of lace, the latter arranged in puffs or else slashed at the side to reveal an under-sleeve of lace ... if one wants to be particularly chic one should wear a fichu of pure white muslin with pleats of the same around the sleeves."

Assuming our own clothes don't get us locked up, what do we do first? Well that smell of fried bacon from John Shorrocks' Grosvenor Dining Rooms is quite tempting, to say nothing of the aroma of oat cakes from Richard Smalley's in Northgate. But this is 1889 and the currency is real gold and real silver with Queen Victoria's head stamped on it. Our decimal coins will be as familiar as Venezuelan bolivars and just about as welcome.

We'll have to rob the Lancashire and Yorkshire bank in Church St., or beg, or get a job. But it's no use setting off for the Job Centre, the Black Greyhound beerhouse is there now. Let's see what the classified ads. have to offer:

"Wanted man with thorough knowledge of Dobbies and Dhooty making to manage shed of 600 looms. Apply Waterside Mill, Darwen."

If you can't tell your Dobbies from your Dhootys, how about this one?

"Wanted clerk, shorthand preferred, but must have excellent longhand."

That wouldn't do for me, my handwritings the sort practised by drunken spiders with inky feet.

There's a firm of gas lighting engineers looking for a representative. Withnell school want an Assistant Master, and there are always openings at Mrs Haworth's register office for servants at Sudell Cross.

I think I'll try the pawnbrokers. There are 19 in Blackburn and the nearest is James Leigh's in Northgate. I don't suppose they'll take the digital watch I got free with petrol, but they might give me something for my wedding ring.

There's no shortage of lodgings in the town, especially if you don't mind sharing a bed with a stranger. Most poor folk supplement their income by taking in lodgers.

What are our chances of surviving our visit unscathed? Well there's good news and there's bad news. First the good news.

The papers are full of adverts for wonderful cure-alls such as *"Du Barry's Revelenta Arabica Food"* which can cure dyspepsia, constipation, indigestion, asthma, bronchitis, consumption, diarrhoea, dysentery, heartburn, typhoid, scarlet fever, diptheria, sea-sickness, morning sickness, eczema, insomnia, paralysis and noises in the ear, and all for 10p a tin from Critchley's chemists in King William St.

Then the bad news. Scarlet fever and measles are on the rampage and with no antibiotics, they're killers. At the beginning of the year Blackburn had a death rate of 44.8 in 1000, the highest in the land. Almost every other house seems to be in mourning. Horse drawn hearses with black plumes are constantly in Whalley New Rd. en route for the cemetery. One out of every four babies born is dead before it reaches twelve months.

The doctors can't cure it and the living conditions of the poor only make it worse. Here's our man at the Blackburn Times again:

"We are now in the vicinity of the homes ... dirty and bare, the windows are well frosted with dust, and many panes are stuffed with rags and paper. The

whole street reeks with a fusty, rancid rottenness, which produces a nauseating feeling ... groups of unwashed women are stood here and there in the doorways, arms akimbo or folded, some of them nursing a rickety child and conversing with coarse ribaldry."

You might think the roads would be safe in 1889. No so. Even with horse drawn vehicles speeding's a problem, only they call it *"furious driving"*, and accidents are common. Fortunately they're rarely fatal.

At least you'd be able to walk the streets at night in safety. I'm afraid not. Newspaper reports of drunkenness and violence are commonplace. A magistrate fines youths for riotous and disorderly conduct and condemns the standard of behaviour of young people in Preston New Road on Sunday nights, when it becomes a popular promenade. The Recorder at the Quarter Sessions deplores the increase in juvenile crime. Even the public library's not safe; its coin collection is stolen by thieves who hide in the building until after closing time.

There's no tele and no video, so what do folk do in their spare time? Well there isn't much spare time. Mill workers do a 56½ hour week, and most shops are open every night until 8.00 including Saturday, and although the half day movement is gaining ground, there are still those who think closing at 1.00 on Thursdays will be the ruin of them.

Even so, there's no shortage of things to do. Apart from the conviviality of the pubs and beerhouses, there's entertainment at three theatres, the Princess', the Theatre Royal, and the Lyceum, where *"Lotto, Lilo and Otto"*, juvenile bike performers, top a bill that includes Maud Ross, dancer and vocalist, *"Comical Cris"* as *"Mephistopheles the Ventriloquist"* and the *"Black Marvel"* Frank Whitely.

There's boating on the lake at Queens Park, skating at the rink in Canterbury St., and Blackburn Rovers have just had a good run in the F.A. Cup, losing to Wolves in the semi-final replay.

Outings to local beauty spots are becoming popular, especially as more and more shops start to close early on Thursdays. Our Blackburn Times man sets the scene:

"The half holiday in Blackburn has been a source of profitable and increased income to the railway companies, and the wagonette and 'bus and cab proprietors of this district. It is astonishing to see the large crowds of people leaving town on any fine Thursday afternoon in June, July, or August ... constantly coming and going are the bicycles and tricycles of modern times. Scores of them, yea hundreds of them in the course of the afternoon."

"Here comes a heavy ancient cart, drawn by four ancient horses. It is crammed full of fat, jolly looking grocers and their wives and sweethearts, quickly outpaced by a trap containing four individuals of the masher type, two of each gender. And on the Whalley Road, the Preston Road, and all other outlets from our communal centre, the dust is stirred until it forms one continuous floury cloud, hovering between the powdered hedge rows of grey-dusted green."

Communications are beginning to shrink the world. Horses still work the tram route on Preston New Road, but lighter tramcars have just been introduced. On the Darwen route steam cars are in operation. There are six trains a day from Blackburn to London. The Post Office delivers letters four times a day, at 7.00 a.m., 12 noon, 4.00 p.m. and 6.30 p.m., and the telephone is beginning to fray nerves in offices and shops all over town. On the continent men called Daimler and Benz are experimenting with horseless carriages.

The world has not yet surrendered all her secrets. Dr. Livingstone's exploits in darkest Africa are still thrilling newspaper readers, and the wild West is still wild. If you felt really adventurous, you could book a passage from Liverpool to New York on the White Star Line for £6.50 from the agents in Montague Street. For myself I think a tram ride to Darwen will be quite adventurous enough.

The tram leaves from outside the old post office in Darwen Street. It's a hot afternoon, so I climb the stairs and sit in the open air on a bench warmed by the sun. The journey to Darwen takes 30 minutes.

I've heard it said that Darwen hasn't changed much in the last 100 years, but one change stands out like an amputated thumb as soon as you reach the Golden Cup. The hill to the West is bare. The Jubilee tower wasn't built until 1897.

Like a sleepy frontier town caught up in a gold rush, Darwen is booming. There's a new market hall, a new railway station, a new hospital at Bull Hill, a new park at Whitehall. The gas works are being improved, and the Peel baths in Railway Road have just been renewed and enlarged.

I alight at the Circus. It's hot, the moors are practically glowing. A lazy farm cart toiling up Bolton Road leaves a boiling of dust in its wake.

Time for a drink and where better than the "Last Rose of Summer" in Bridge Street? It's dark inside and there are stone flagged floors, rough wooden benches and whitewashed walls. The ale, brewed at Spring Vale brewery rushes out of the barrel as eagerly as a moorland stream. Never mind the foreign bodies, it tastes fine.

With beer at 5p a gallon and 27 beerhouses and 49 inns in Darwen, there couldn't be a better time and place for a pub crawl.

Across the Circus there's the Angel, just about where the pelican crossing outside the post office is now. Up on the Green there's a more familiar sight, the White Lion, but it stands at the edge of a warren of slums and cheap lodging houses. They're to be cleared soon to make way for the Model, but some of the characters drinking there are just a little too 'picturesque' for comfort.

Moderation is true temperance, so after a visit to another familiar sight, the Greenway, it's time for a stroll. Crossing Duckworth Street be careful where you put your feet. The smell of fresh horse manure is quite pungent. Better than petrol fumes though.

The sight of Union Street would make you stagger, even if you hadn't had a drink. There's no fire station, no police station, no health centre, no school, and no library looking down from on high. New Mill occupies the site and its chimney casts a long shadow.

There's quite a crowd chattering excitedly on the pavement outside the Theatre Royal in Railway Road. The sun is dipping low over the moors, and it's time to head back to the tram, working itself up into a lather for the trip back to Blackburn. Time too to digest our impressions of 1889 and wonder if we'd want to stay for good.

The world is still innocent. The horrors of two world wars are yet unknown. The dangers of pollution and nuclear power are undreamt of. For the well-to-do, life is sweet.

At grand houses along Richmond Terrace and up Preston New Road servants are preparing for supper parties and Summer balls. A contemporary source gives some hints for entertainers:

"Cold roast chicken is a safe supper dish to provide, it being particularly in request among ladies. Salmon and lobster appear in almost as many forms as does chicken. Game pie is a very popular dish. Sandwiches of potted game,

chicken, or lobster are invariably given, and every menu comprises jelly. Light French confectionery is supposed to put the finishing touches to a well-arranged supper table."

"Champagne is always given at a ball supper. Some ball givers provide a variety of mineral water, apollinaris etc., in addition to soda and seltzer water, which are drunk with champagne, sherry and brandy. Brandy at 7s (35p) a bottle is the quality usually given."

But for most there was little comfort and less luxury. When the factory whistle blows at 5.00 on a cold dark morning, there's no central heating boiler humming away, no light at the flick of a switch, no wall to wall carpets, no bathroom, no hot water, no fridge, no toaster, no radio, no television.

If you don't feel well, there's no phone ro ring in sick, and if you need the doctor, he won't come unless you can pay, and with no antibiotics, even if he does come he might not be able to cure you.

No, perhaps the best thing after all would be to nod off on the hard bench of the tram, as the sunset sanctifies Billinge Hill, and wake up on the upholstered seat of a modern bus as it rolls into a bustling, brightly lit Boulevard.

I don't think you'd miss much, except perhaps the smell of oat cakes from Smalley's in Northgate, and perhaps that pint in Darwen at the Last Rose of Summer.

DARWEN

BLACKBURN

BLACKBURN.

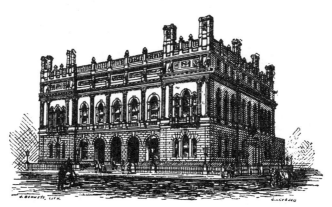

The Town Hall.

COMMERCE AND INDUSTRY.

LTHOUGH at the present day one of the most important of the many industrial centres which assist in retaining for Lancashire its world-wide fame, the town of Blackburn cannot lay claim to much historical or traditional antiquity. It is surmised by one of the local historians (Dr. Whittaker) that there was a castle at Blackburn, occupied by the Roman-British chiefs, and subsequently by the Saxons; but there is certainly no vestige of such a building, and the site is a matter of tradition alone. What is certain is, that at the time of the Conquest the country for miles around the little brook which gave its name to the town was of a barren and unattractive character, fringed by a forest in which the nobles of the time found the pleasures of the chase, and that it was bestowed by the Norman monarch upon Albert de Lacy, one of those who had assisted him in his ever-memorable expedition. From this worthy gentleman the manor would seem to have passed through several families, and notably that of the Fauconbergs, to whom it came by the marriage of the eldest son of the first viscount of that name. It was the son of this gentleman, the second viscount, who married Mary, the third daughter of Oliver Cromwell, and whose nuptials are said to have been celebrated at Hampton Court with great pomp and lustre. Later in the century (1689) he was created Earl of Fauconbridge by William III., but the title died with him, and thirty years later the connection of the family with the manor was broken by its sale, for the sum of £8,650, to Messrs. Baldwin, Feilden, and Sudell, names which are well known in local history.

"Through all these centuries," says Mr. W. A. Abram, J.P., F.R.H.S., in his "History of Blackburn," from which we quote by permission, "Blackburn remained a non-corporate town, without castle, abbey, or other structural feature to dignify its aspect to the eye of the passing pilgrim. Its church of St. Marie, founded before the Conquest, was the single object capable of attracting notice among the cluster of timber-framed tenements that formed the town. The lords of the manor of Blackburn had from an early date been non-resident, and there was no knightly family of repute and power to reflect some of its lustre upon the place, no goodly manorial hall within the vill to lift its front boldly above the level uniformity of the tenements of yeomen, husbandmen, and craftsmen. . . . . Onward into the Tudor period Blackburn was still a town obscure and little known of strangers, being quite out of the track of travellers performing the journey between London and the south, and the northern counties and Scotland. Leland, the first English itinerant antiquary of note, who was in Lancashire about 1540, does not seem to have looked at Blackburn, and does not name the town. James Pilkington, the zealous Bishop of Durham, visited Blackburn in 1564, observing church affairs. Of the moral condition of the town the good Bishop draws a melancholy picture; of its material aspect he remarks nothing. The old church had been partially rebuilt a few years before, and looked much the same edifice it was until it was taken down in 1820. In the churchyard were the vicarage and school-house, both dilapidated, and calling for replacement in 1564. The street plan of the town was an irregular cross. . . . . The population would not exceed two thousand people. Such was Blackburn when Elizabeth ascended the throne, and such it stood, with but slight change or increase, until the beginning of last century."

INDUSTRIAL PROGRESS.

But if Blackburn falls short in antiquarian interest, there is plenty of compensation to be found in a survey of the industrial progress to which it owes its present position and prosperity. As long ago as the time of good Queen Bess Blackburn was described as "a noted market town," but less than a century later it had become noted for one particular article of the staple trade of the county which was produced there with better success than in any other place. It was called "Blackburn Check," and was a species of cloth consisting of a linen warp and cotton woof, one or both being dyed in the thread, which gave the piece, when woven, a checked or striped appearance. This fabric was afterwards superseded by the "Blackburn Gray," so-called because the material of which it was composed were not dyed but were sent to the printers unbleached, or in the "gray" state. It was about the middle of the seventeenth century that Lewis Roberts, in a work

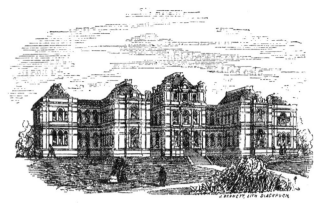

BLACKBURN INFIRMARY.

entitled "The Treasure of Traffic," made the first published reference to the manufacture of cotton goods in England, and in the many changes which the industry has undergone since that period, Blackburn has taken no unimportant part, several inventions owing their origin to natives of the town. The application of machinery to the preparation and spinning of raw cotton preceded by some years the inventions of Arkwright and Crompton, it being not much later than 1760 or 1761 when James Hargreaves of Blackburn invented a carding engine, to be followed a few years later by a spinning jenny, containing eight spindles, made to revolve by means of bands from a horizontal wheel. Subsequently the number of spindles was increased to eighty, and the events which followed have already been referred to in our notice of Lancashire industry. Hargreaves had to fly from his native county after his house had been broken into and his machine destroyed, and for a long time there was a feeling of intense opposition to the introduction of any labour-saving machinery, the spinners being of opinion that anything which increased the facility of production must necessarily be to their detriment—an industrial fallacy which seems almost too silly to deserve mention in these days. Some men with longer heads than their brethren took up the idea patented by Hargreaves, and machines were again introduced, but the spinners rose *en masse* throughout the district, and endeavoured to wreak their vengeance upon the unoffending apparatus. Blackburn took a prominent part in these disturbances, not only doing all the mischief that was possible within its own boundaries, but sending out bands of discontented iconoclasts to Darwen and other places. By this means the industry was driven for a time into the adjoining counties, principally to Nottingham; but in course of time better ideas prevailed, and the folly of resistance to what was really most beneficial was generally admitted, greatly to the advantage of the Lancastrians as a whole. Hargreaves' invention was used for some time, but it was open to some objections, which were partially removed by Arkwright, and wholly by Crompton, a native of Bolton, whose story we have referred to in our notice of that town. Thus it was that these men laid the foundation of a great and ever-increasing industry, which has been the means of elevating Lancashire to a permanent position in the manufacturing annals of the kingdom, which has caused populous and busy hives of men and women to arise almost out of the desert, and which has made Blackburn that which it is to-day. Forty years ago it was stated in a work of reference that the annual value of manufactured goods sent out of Blackburn was two millions and a half; to-day it cannot be less than ten millions,

for the town is admittedly the largest and most important manufacturing centre in the world, so far as cotton is concerned. Large and well-built factories abound on every hand, some of them giving employment to as many as two thousand hands, and nowhere in the world can there be found more perfect machinery and appliances than those which are at the service of the Blackburn weavers, or men and women more thoroughly acquainted with their trade. Every improvement that science could suggest or ingenuity could contrive calculated to advance production, or conduce to the comfort and convenience of the worker, has been adopted, and if some of those who slaved by day and night in the cotton mills of fifty years ago could now "revisit the glimpses of the moon" they would be vastly surprised at the changes which have come over the spirit of the scene. Legislation, education, and the natural progress of events have been important factors in the improvements which have been made. The employers have recognised that in dealing with operatives they are meeting human beings like themselves, and not mere automata, wound up for a certain period and then to be thrown aside. The operatives themselves, emancipated from thraldom, educated both politically and generally, better fed and better housed, are of a different class altogether to their predecessors, and the dignity of labour is fully apparent in the working men and women of Blackburn and other Lancashire towns. There have been differences of opinion between the two classes, as is natural in any circumstances, but they have not, since the days of "The Long Strike," been of a serious character, and there is every reason to hope that in future they may be amicably settled, without any shadow of resort to the rough-and-ready methods of a past generation. Many operatives, indeed, are in the position of employers themselves, for nowhere in England has the spirit of co-operation been more widely developed than in Lancashire, and many a large and busy mill and factory is the property of those who tend its engines and work its machinery. The spirit of self-reliance and independence thus engendered has not been without an appreciable effect upon the characters of the people, and nowhere, unless perhaps in the neighbouring county of Yorkshire, is there a more self-reliant, pushing, and go-ahead people than in such places as Blackburn, Bolton, Oldham, and the larger towns of the county.

Writing in or about 1830, a critic remarks that "the police regulations in Blackburn are very defective. Having no municipal

ST. MARY'S CHURCH.

government, the duties of preserving the public peace devolve upon irresponsible persons, and a sort of supreme authority is vested in two officers, annually elected, one for the higher and the other for the lower division of the hundred. The parochial concerns are managed by a select vestry." This was hardly a complimentary view to take of affairs in Blackburn at the period, but it was doubtless a true one. Soon after that was written, however, the iron roads began to bring the town into closer connection with other parts of the county and kingdom; increased convenience of communication brought greater trade; population multiplied to a large extent, from 36,629 in 1831, to 63,126 in 1851; and the old-fangled system of local government soon went by the board, eventuating, in the year 1851, in the receipt of a charter of incorporation. Since the advent of a mayor and corporation, there has been little or no reason to complain of the municipal government of Blackburn. Broad well-paved thoroughfares abound, curved and ugly corners have been improved; the gas and water supply has been made as complete as possible; new public offices have been provided for the transaction of the hundred and one departments of municipal business; open spaces for the recreation of the people have been secured; education has been studied in various ways; and, in a word, the progress of the town and the comfort of its residents have been well considered and worked for by those whom the latter have selected to carry on the business of municipal government.

Blackburn has been a market town for three centuries past—we have already noted Camden's remark—and in 1649 it was reported that "in Blackburn there is every Monday a market, and some fairs." Later in the same century the town was noted for the great weekly market which was held for the sale of cattle, corn, and provisions on Mondays. In 1774 this market was made twice

TRINITY WESLEYAN CHAPEL, PRESTON NEW ROAD.

The municipal government of the town has its executive centre at the Town Hall, an edifice in the Italian style, erected in the year 1856, at a cost of some £30,000. Here the council meet for the transaction of business, and here are the offices of the borough surveyor, the town clerk, the burial board, and other local and administrative officials and bodies. The present head of the corporation is Captain John Rutherford, a worthy successor to the municipal magnates who have preceded him in the office of mayor. The petty sessions are also held in the Town Hall, and the borough has its own quarter sessions, Mr. Miles W. Mattinson, M.P., being the recorder, and Mr. W. E. L. Gaine, town clerk. Among the other public buildings are the Exchange, a Gothic building of large and handsome dimensions, erected in 1865; the Infirmary, a noble and useful institution which dates from 1862; the Mechanics' Institute, the Public Baths, the Free Library, and various educational and other edifices, including the Grammar School, which was founded by Queen Elizabeth in 1567, and reorganized in 1877. It is managed by governors, and the subjects are, classics, divinity, mathematics, natural sciences, general literature, and English subjects. There is one scholarship tenable at any university. There is also the handsome and commendable Technical School, the first stone of which was laid by the Prince of Wales, on the occasion of his visit to the town last year (1888), an event of no small importance to the burgesses, who gave his Royal Highness a right royal welcome, and made the most of an occasion which in the natural order of things cannot be of frequent recurrence. As regards open spaces, Blackburn is well situate, having the Corporation Park, which covers an

weekly (Wednesday and Saturday) and the arrangement is still adhered to, Blakey Moor being the site. As regards fairs, Mr. Abram records that the first great fair for cattle and produce was held on the 1st of May, 1583. In Rider's "Fairs," 1746, Blackburn Fair is still fixed for May-day. Not many years later two additional fairs were appointed in the year, on Easter Monday and at Michaelmas (October 17th). The market accommodation at the present day is very extensive, and farmers and graziers still come from far and near to Blackburn, to dispose of their produce and cattle. The market tolls for the open and covered markets are let by auction for two years, and the present lessee is paying for that term the large sum of £12,450, which goes far to substantiate the claim of Blackburn market to be one of the busiest and best paying institutions of the kind in the whole of the United Kingdom.

expanse of fifty acres, at an altitude of 700 feet above the sea level. The splendid views of the country round which can be obtained from this eminence, the health-giving breezes which are always playing around it, and the excellent arrangement of the park render it a pleasant and popular resort for the sons and daughters of toil. In addition to this, there is the Jubilee Park, which, as its name implies, was opened on Jubilee Day, 1887, and remains a very sensible memorial of the great national event. This park has an area of 35 acres, and is in every way pleasantly situate.

With regard to locomotion Blackburn is well supplied. Half a century ago people were only just beginning to find out the necessity which existed for means of communication, and that even the Leeds and Liverpool Canal (which cost a million and a quarter and took nearly half a century to complete) was not all they required. In 1843 parliamentary sanction was given to the scheme of the East Lancashire Railway Company, which projected a line from Preston to Blackburn, Accrington, and Colne, and on the

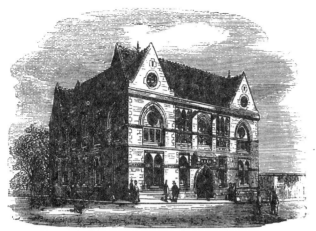

FREE LIBRARY AND MUSEUM.

19th June, 1846, Blackburn and Preston were linked together by the iron way, the first train over this section running on that day. One can well imagine the curiosity with which the new arrangement was regarded—the fears which were expressed as to the safety of the passengers, and the doubts as to the stability of the concern. In 1848 communication was opened between Bolton and Blackburn, and in 1869 a new and direct route was opened to Manchester, Liverpool, &c. The railways are now the property of the Lancashire and Yorkshire Railway Company, who, with the London and North-Western Company, supplied the means of communication with all parts of the kingdom from the handsome and commodious Central Station, which is used by the two companies in common. There are several suburban stations, and the train service is frequent and well arranged. Steam tramways and omnibuses run to and from all parts of the town, and there is an efficient supply of cabs and flies.

THE PARISH CHURCH.

The old parish church of St. Marie, which was for a very long time the only public building in Blackburn, was of Norman foundation. It was taken down and rebuilt in 1820. In 1831 the new structure was partially destroyed by fire and was once more restored, taking then the form in which it now stands, and winning general admiration by the beauty of the building. It is a large and handsome edifice in the Gothic style of the fourteenth century, consisting of nave, chancel, north and south aisles, western tower and porches. At the west end is a handsome three-storied tower. In 1875 the interior was renovated and rebenched and a new organ erected, at the personal cost of Mr. William Coddington. There are nearly fifteen hundred sittings, of which about one-half are free. There is a good peal of ten bells, six of which date from 1737. There are a number of other churches belonging to the Establishment in the town and district, but they are mostly of modern erection. They possess more or less architectural beauty, and are generally well adapted to the purpose they are intended to serve. The Nonconformists from an early date have had meeting-houses in Blackburn, and some of these edifices at the present day will stand very well in comparison with those of the Church as by Law Established. They are numerous and well attended, and represent every sect from the followers of John Wesley and Calvin to the members of the Salvation Army.

PARLIAMENTARY REPRESENTATION.

Blackburn has been a Parliamentary borough, returning two members, since the year 1832. The electors number 16,329, and at the general election in 1886 Messrs. William Coddington (C) and William Henry Hornby (C) were returned unopposed.

THE LOCAL PRESS.

Blackburn is particularly well represented in connection with the Fourth Estate. The *Blackburn Evening Press* and *Standard*, with offices in Fishergate, are the property of a company, and profess Conservative and Liberal Unionist principles. The *Express* was founded to afford adequate representation to these views in Blackburn and surrounding districts, and was subsequently incorporated with the *Standard*, a weekly Conservative paper founded so far back as 1832. Mr. W. H. Barnett is editor of the daily, whilst Mr. Abrams, a local historian of considerable reputation, is in editorial charge of the weekly edition. Both journals are produced in a first-class style, contain an immense variety of news from all parts of the county, the latest market and political information, and the *Standard* makes a speciality of local history and antiquities. The *Blackburn Times*, a Liberal organ, was established in 1854, and is published by Messrs. John and George Soulmier. It is the oldest penny weekly in South-East Lancashire, and has a circulation of 14,500. It is edited by Mr. John G. Shaw, and is a capitally arranged, well-printed, and interesting journal. "Bits of Old Lancashire" form a special feature in its columns. The *Northern Daily Telegraph* is an evening journal, established so recently as 1886, but already achieving a success which is unique in the history of provincial newspaper enterprise. Its circulation is officially stated at over forty thousand copies a day, and this cannot be wondered at when the extent and variety of its general and local news is considered. There are six or seven editions daily, with all the latest sporting, political, and other news. The chief office is at Railway Road, Blackburn, Mr. Thomas P. Ritzema being the publisher, and there are branch offices at Market Place, Darwen; Guildhall Street, Preston; Dutton Street, Accrington; Hammerton Street, Burnley; Drake Street, Rochdale; Tulketh Street, Stockport; and at Halifax, Dewsbury, Huddersfield, Bury,

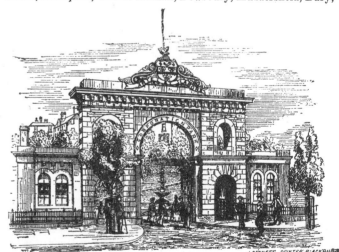

BLACKBURN PARK ENTRANCE.

and Barrow in Furness. The *Cricketers' Herald and Football Times*, published by Mr. C. Walmesby, Fielden Street, represents a branch of sport which is dear to the hearts of Lancashire folk. It is published every Tuesday at one penny. The *Blackburn Spy*, fortnightly, one penny, is a critical and satirical journal, published by Mr. F. J. Holloway.

BLACKBURN.

>•<

THE ATTENTION OF OUR READERS IS NOW DIRECTED TO THE RISE AND PROGRESS OF LEADING BUSINESS
HOUSES OF BLACKBURN. IT IS TO SUCH FIRMS, IRRESPECTIVE OF THEIR MAGNITUDE,
THAT BLACKBURN OWES HER GROWTH AND IMPORTANCE

Star Paper Mill Company, Ld., Feniscowles, near Blackburn.—One of the leading and most scientific industries of the century finds a representation befitting its importance in the works of the Star Paper Mill Company, Feniscowles, near Blackburn, which were established in the year 1875 in the existing premises by the present proprietors. The premises occupied by this Company cover an area of thirteen acres of ground, and employ a working staff of over three hundred hands. These works are furnished with eight large Lancashire boilers, and the combined horse-power of the various engines at work is about two thousand. These works are capable of turning out 200 tons weekly, which is entirely consumed in the production of "news" papers. The surface appearance of the buildings is by no means so attractive as the curious and interesting processes which are to be seen within, and their extent is much greater than at first sight would seem. Passing by the offices the boiler-house is reached. This building contains eight large boilers. In addition to providing steam for various other purposes, these boilers supply the motive power for several sets of engines, two of which, flanking the works, indicate 500 and 800 horse-power respectively. Another engine of 40 indicated horse-power is employed in connection with the electric lighting of the works, and a fourth engine manipulates the precautionary arrangements for the emergency of fire. Considering the inflammatory nature of a vast quantity of the material stored and used at the works, it is remarkable that there has not been an outbreak of fire since the inauguration of the concern thirteen years ago. The consumption of coal in the boiler-house (to which place the fuel is brought down by an inclined tramway, worked with an endless wire rope, from the Leeds and Liverpool Canal, which runs close by) is upwards of 400 tons per week. A similar tramway is employed to convey the material—rags, straw, grass, lime, soda, &c.—from the boats to the various storage places, which are very conveniently arranged for the ultimate distribution of these articles. The visitor at once proceeds to the mixing and dusting rooms. These, it should be explained, are situated on the second storey of an extensive pile of buildings which forms the only exception to the general structural design of the premises. The remaining buildings are all erected in the form of sheds and are arranged to adjoin each other, thus occupying a large area of ground. Prior to manipulation in the dusters, the rags are "sorted," this operation being generally performed by the rag dealers who supply the article. The two dusters consist of revolving octagonal wire cylinders, narrowing towards the end in which the rags are inserted. By the friction caused by the revolution of the cylinders the dust is partially released, and falls through into a receptacle provided for the purpose, from whence it is conveyed away by farmers and used as a fertiliser. Here is seen another illustration of the economy of natural commerce. The rags gravitate towards the larger opening and discharge themselves automatically. From 60 to 70 tons of these waste rags are weekly operated upon at the Star Mills. Other substances, such as waste flax and Bombay gunny bagging (a native manufactured jute), are introduced into the rags, and the whole, after being received from the duster, is carefully examined by girls, who remove all foreign materials, such as those supplied in ladies' corsets and "improvers," and gentlemen's discarded linen. The rags are then taken in skips to the chopping machine in an adjoining room, where the fibre is separated by a revolving iron disc, with a series of knives attached, working upon a fixed blade at the head of the machine. They are now placed in a second duster in another room, and afterwards passed through another chopper, which divides the fibre more finely. The men engaged in this work, owing to the atmosphere being heavily laden with unpleasant dust released from the waste, have their breathing apparatus protected by a curious trunk-like appendage covering the nose and mouth. The heterogeneous fibrous mass is then admitted, through trap doors, to the "kiers," or boilers, below. There are fifteen of these kiers, some of which are employed for boiling rags, and the others for straw and Esparto grass. The rag kiers accommodate 50 cwts. of rags, which are treated with a solution of lime. The whole then revolves horizontally, and during the revolution of the kier steam is injected into it, and the seething process is continued for twelve hours. With straw and Esparto grass a solution of caustic soda is employed instead of the lime to kill all glutinous and silicious substances. The Esparto grass (in order to preserve the whole length of the

fibre and thus enhance the value of the paper) is boiled in upright kiers, in which, by a vomiting pipe, the liquor is constantly kept in circulation, completely saturating the fibre. When sufficiently boiled, the caustic soda is drawn off and conveyed to a tank for evaporation. Hot water is then introduced, and in its turn drained off, and the grass is afterwards removed by manual labour. The liquor from the straw kiers is also conveyed away for evaporation, but in the act of revolving the kier discharges its contents through a kind of trap door, manual labour thus being superseded. The evaporation of the caustic soda is a very wise provision, as the recovered soda is only slightly reduced in strength. The process also possesses the advantage that it avoids the necessity of polluting the adjoining natural waterway with the whole of the refuse liquor. Before following the further progress of the fibrous materials, the important incidental process of the preparation of the caustic soda requires attention. It is carried on in a spacious shed adjoining the two-storeyed erection before spoken of. On the ground floor of this latter building vast quantities of carbonate of soda are stored in sacks. This substance is mixed with an ordinary solution of lime in a series of tanks, and the whole agitated by a revolving agitator, and then allowed to settle. The lime, dross, and other solid refuse matter is precipitated to the bottom of the tanks, or pans, and the clear solution of caustic soda is drawn off by a syphon pipe to a tank below, from whence it is pumped, when required, to the kiers. In the same room the process of preparing the chloride of lime for the purpose of bleaching the pulp is carried on. Chloride of lime is mixed with water in pans having a large capacity, and then agitated, afterwards being allowed to settle. To return to the boiled materials. After boiling, they are conveyed in tubs to the washing and bleaching room, another spacious building, containing fifteen engines or machines. Three of these have each a capacity of 35 cwts., and the remaining twelve of 15 cwts. each. The rags, straw, and grass (the two last-named substances being mixed together in certain proportions) are placed in separate machines—large, open tanks, with a revolving perpendicular disc in the centre. Cold water is poured into the tank, and the matter which it contains is kept in circulation by the revolving disc, to which blades are attached. These bear upon a permanent horizontal blade, by means of which the fibre is drawn to any required fineness. A wire-gauze cylinder, with buckets—in the form of hoppers—adhering to it inside, is also made to revolve and draw off the dirty water into a compartment of the tank, from whence it is conveyed away by drains to settling tanks. When sufficiently washed, the water is substituted by the solution of chloride of lime previously spoken of, for bleaching purposes, and the matter is brought to any required degree of whiteness, the machine being at work during the whole time bleaching is proceeding. This completed, the pulp is passed to the drainer house adjoining; this is a capacious building containing a quantity of "tanks," each capable of holding 15 cwts. of pulp. The "tanks" are brick compartments, open at the top and having a perforated zinc floor, about 10 feet by 7 feet by 3 feet in dimensions. Whilst draining the chloride of lime passes through the floor of the tanks to a well beneath, and is again employed for the same purpose of bleaching. The pulp remains about an hour in the drainers, and it is then shovelled into waggons, mixed together, and conveyed to the "beating" engines—so called because they supersede the ancient process of beating the pulp by hand. There are 26 of these engines, each accommodating about 400 lbs. of the mixed pulp, which, when first placed in the engines, is of a very heavy consistency. By an arrangement of revolving knives the consistency of the pulp is reduced to one closely resembling milk, the "beating" process occupying four hours. Sizing and colouring matter are also introduced, when required, whilst the pulp is being manipulated in the "beaters," where also, by means of cold water, the residual chemical compounds are washed out of the pulp. The fibrous mass, having been reduced to the desired consistency (and, consequently, length of fibre), is passed into large chests, and then pumped into chests elevated above the paper machines; each of the three machines is supplied with three chests, each capable of holding 1,200 lbs. of pulp. After being allowed to pass through three strainers, the pulp at length reaches the paper machines. These are four in number, two being 127 inches wide, the third 112 inches, and the fourth 102 inches in width. The principle of the paper machines is, roughly, conveying the pulp round a series of slowly revolving cylinders, the width of the machine, covered with felt. Before arriving at these cylinders it is carried over an endless wire trough, which vibrates laterally and mixes the fibres together, at the same time straining water from the pulp. A suction box, at the termination of the wire trough and adjoining the "dandy"—a revolving roller of wire gauze, placed immediately over the trough and bearing the design with which it is intended to stamp the paper—effectually removes all remaining liquid water from the pulp. It then passes between two brass rollers, which press the pulp together and form the paper. As yet, however, the paper only possesses the necessary thickness, and is moist to the point of saturation. Each side of the sheet is then made to run between two iron press bowls, which place the "surface" on it. The paper then passes to the drying cylinders, each of 4 feet 6 inches diameter. There are seventeen of these cylinders on each machine, and as they are heated with steam, the paper, in its passage over them, ultimately becomes dry, and is at length received on reels at the end of the machine. At the time of our visit the paper in process of manufacture on one machine was intended for exportation ; that on the other three machines for home consumption. It must be clearly understood that these machines from where the thin liquid pulp leaves the strainers to where it emerges as paper are perfectly continuous, the numerous cylinders being arranged one above the other, in order to bring the machine into as small a compass as possible. If the paper, as is usually the case, is not required to be the total width of the machine, cutters, or sharp revolving discs, are arranged, as desired, to divide the paper before its reception on the final cylinder, or reel. Should the paper break during its passage through the machine, one of the divided ends is guided on to a cylinder, and the sheet, being elastic in its nature while in that state, rapidly covers the whole width of the cylinder. The production of the paper is at the rate of, on each machine, about 200 feet a minute. All that now remains is to prepare the paper for leaving the premises. The greater quantity is taken into a reeling room, where the edges of the paper are trimmed, and the paper itself is passed on to a roll, or reel, in a continuous length of between four and five miles, according to order. There are seven reeling machines at work. There are also other mechanical arrangements for cutting up the rolls of paper removed from the machine into sheets of any required size. These are then removed into another room, where females are employed in picking out any broken or torn sheets. The paper is then packed in reams of 500 sheets. A considerable number of men, and several hydraulic presses, are employed in securely packing both the reels and the reams, especially those intended for exportation. By a calculation of the periods occupied in the varied processes, it will be found that in about twenty hours waste rags brought to the works can be converted into paper. Before leaving the Star Paper Mill, which employs some 300 people (in alternate shifts, as the machinery is run uninterruptedly from Monday morning to Saturday noon) and produce the largest quantity of "news" paper of any similar works in the United Kingdom, it may be noted that the premises are lighted by electricity, the electric lighting apparatus having been fitted up by Mr. Thomas Barton, of Ainsworth Street, Blackburn. A Brush dynamo is driven by an engine of 40 indicated horse-power, and there are 300 lamps utilised in lighting the works. The company is regulated and governed by five directors, of whom A. F. Bentley, Esq., is chairman ; and the duties of management meet with an able and efficient discharge at the hands of Mr. Joseph Turner, and Mr. J. E. Jepson, who has acted as secretary for the last thirteen years, the entire concern being one of the most successful engaged in this class of business in Lancashire, and the quality of its production is well-known throughout the United Kingdom and the Colonies.

Eleanor Mercer, Mineral Water Manufacturer, Borough Mineral Water Works, Mill Lane, Blackburn.—The industry of the manufacture of mineral waters is thoroughly represented in Blackburn in the well-known and old-established house of Eleanor Mercer, whose premises, known as the Borough Mineral Water Works, are situated in Mill Lane, and the firm deserves honourable recognition amongst these sketches on account of its being one of the foremost of the kind in this district of Lancashire. The business was founded in the year 1858, under the title of Hummer & Mercer, in Barton Street, whence they removed to Spring Gardens, where the business was successfully carried on until the premises here were taken over by the Corporation, when they again removed to the present large establishment in Mill Lane. In 1870 the firm of Hummer & Mercer was dissolved, Mr. Mercer continuing the business until his death, which took place in 1877, when it was taken over by his widow, who is now the sole proprietress. Borough Mineral Water Works cover a large area of ground and are equipped in first-rate style with all the most approved machinery and appliances for producing mineral waters of every description. The plant comprises several machines by McEwen of Manchester, Galloway of Bolton, and Cooper of Manchester, Hayward and Tyler of London, &c., all being of the most approved designs, and these beautiful machines are kept constantly busy in producing the excellent beverages for which the house is now so famous. This firm was the first to introduce ginger ale and split sodas. The trade of the firm, in which a large staff of hands are employed, with five horses and carts for delivering the goods, extends throughout Blackburn and to a distance of fifteen miles around the town in every direction, the business connection being with the most influential houses. Among the secrets of this firm's success are, their having an abundant supply of spring water, which is pronounced to be perfect in its chemical qualities for the production of mineral waters ;

their using only the most approved drugs and pure materials ; and sparing no expense in plant where an outlay will tend to improve or maintain the excellent quality of the beverages produced, while their purity is guaranteed by the fact that samples are frequently submitted to Mr. G. H. Sharpe, F.C.S., of London, for analysis. Mrs. Eleanor Mercer, the proprietress of this business, is an agreeable, courteous lady and possessing business abilities of a high order, she continues to maintain and extend the old-established reputation of the firm for high-class manufactures, promptitude in executing orders, and honourable methods in the management of the business.

Richard Ryden, Machinery Merchant, Oil and Tallow Refiner, and Complete Mill Furnisher, and Licensed Valuer, Albert Works, Blackburn.—The textile industries are second in importance and usefulness only to those of agriculture, and the busy mills of Blackburn and the surrounding districts, which tend so greatly to the prosperity of this district, are constantly requiring parts of machinery and other requisites to meet tear and wear. Amongst the firms upon which these works and other steam users depend for their supply of these necessaries, honourable mention is deserved by that of Richard Ryden, machinery merchant, oil and tallow refiner, and complete mill furnisher, whose extensive warehouses and works are situated at New Water Street, known as Albert Works ; Oil and Tallow Refinery, Mary Ellen Street ; Warehouse, Commercial Mills, Blackburn. The business, which is the most extensive of its kind in Blackburn, was established in the present premises in the year 1880 by Mr. Ryden, who is still the sole proprietor. The warehouses are of large extent, occupying a building of three storeys in height, and covering a large area of ground. They are admirably fitted up and arranged, and consist of a handsome office, with six spacious warehouses, three of which measure 25 yards square. The classes of goods exhibited comprise hundreds of power looms by various makers, the reed spaces of which vary from 35 inches to 130 inches, tape-sizing machines, warping mills, winding frames, size becks, Green's economizers, dobbies, tons of twill motions, spring tops, tons of loom fittings, weighing machines, drums, 2,000 pairs of loom pulleys, and other articles of a like nature which space prevents our noting in detail, amongst which are engines, boilers, and all kinds of spinning and weaving machinery. Besides this class of goods, the firm's warehouse display fifteen varieties of sizing materials used in the same industries, and every description of goods that could be found in the stores of weaving and spinning mills, such as leather strapping, strap butts, check straps, &c., ropes, twines, cloths, flannels, pickers, springs, baskets, brushes, &c. The firm's oil and tallow works, situate in Mary Ellen Street, have recently been thoroughly equipped, with a refining and mixing plant, and of their products a valuable stock is also kept in the warehouses, comprising mineral oils, loom oils, spindle oils, sperm oils, neat's-foot oils, finest amber cylinder oil, castor oil, tallow, &c. The trade of this house is very extensive, and reaches all over England and to some foreign parts, a very large business being done in oils and tallow, the excellent quality and moderate prices of which having won for the house a high reputation not only amongst mills, but also engineers and steam users of every kind. He is also a large buyer of bankrupt stocks, trustees and others finding him of great convenience in securing a reasonable price with prompt cash, thereby saving them the delay and annoyance usually accompanying sales by auction, &c. Mr. Ryden, the proprietor of this important business has recently purchased the Whalley Bank Mills, six stories in height, with large yard, which he intends to utilise as a centre for warehousing, and oil and tallow refinery, continuing office and store at New Water Street. He is well known as a machinery valuer, and the honourable methods that have always characterized the management of his business in every department have won for him a high place in the esteem and confidence of his numerous influential supporters.

Joseph Appleby & Sons, Daisyfield Corn Mills, Blackburn.—This business was established about fifty years ago by Mr. Joseph Appleby, and is now carried on by his two sons, Edgar and Arthur Appleby, in conjunction with enterprises of a similar character at Bootle, Liverpool, Burnley, and Clayton-le-Moors. The Daisyfield Corn Mills occupy a commanding position on the Lancashire and Yorkshire Railway Company, and on the banks of the Leeds and Liverpool Canal, and are fitted with the latest and most approved style of milling machinery for a capacity of about 3,000 sacks of flour per week. The building is six storeys high, divided into four divisions—the granary, mill, screen-rooms, and silos, all protected by a complete installation of Grinnell's Sprinklers for the extinction of fire. The silos will hold 20,000 sacks of wheat. Suitable conveniences also exist for the preparation of oats, beans, Indian corn, and peas, for cattle food. The works are supplied with electric light. Mr. Edgar Appleby was elected Jubilee Mayor, and accepted office a second time on the occasion of the first visit of royalty to Blackburn, when T.R.H. the Prince and Princess of Wales laid the foundation stone of the Technical School, and were suitably entertained by Mr. Appleby.

King William Street, Blackburn, with the Market Hall clock majestically
surveying the scene.

Blackburn. Preston New Road.

A view of Preston New Road, which would be familiar to the folk of a century ago, although taken slightly nearer the turn of the century.

Another view of Preston New Road showing the entrance to Corporation Park.

W. Farnworth, Pharmaceutical Chemist and Manufacturer of Mineral Waters, the Pharmacy, 49, King William Street (opposite the Market House), Blackburn. — One of the most notable names in connection with pharmacy in Blackburn and the country surrounding is that of Mr. W. Farnworth, whose business was founded by the present proprietor as far back as the year 1841. The house originated at premises elsewhere in Blackburn, but removed to the present eligible address in 1855. These premises were designed by Mr. Farnworth, and erected by him specially to meet the requirements of his important and superior trade. As a first-class pharmaceutical establishment they are unsurpassed. The building has a fine frontage to King William Street, and is most handsomely appointed throughout. It contains one of the choicest stocks of drugs, chemicals, and pharmaceutical preparations, pomades, perfumes, soaps, toilet requisites, and other chemists' specialties to be found in the county; and each item in this superior assortment of goods has been selected with the most careful regard to quality and reliability. Nothing of an inferior nature is permitted on the premises. An important business is done in patent medicines and proprietary articles of all kinds; and in these Mr. Farnworth deals only with preparations of established repute, being careful never to lend the influence and aid of his well-known name to any medicine of unknown character or untried efficacy. Requisites for the sick room constitute another notable feature in the stock of this pharmacy, the newest and best devices and productions for the convenience of nurses and invalids being well represented; and a full stock is held in surgical appliances of the kinds most generally in demand—such as trusses, elastic stockings, abdominal belts, bandages, &c., all of which are kept on the premises in great variety. In toilet articles Mr. Farnworth has every description of choice perfumery, satchet powders, eau de Cologne of

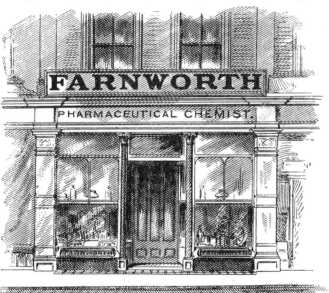

genuine manufacture, smelling-bottles, &c.; and his stock of the various articles in use on the toilet table, hair-brushes, dressing-combs, nail, tooth, and shaving brushes, &c., is one of the largest and best in Blackburn. Turning again to the drug department, we find that homœopathy is duly represented by a complete assortment of the various preparations, tinctures, &c., advocated by that branch of the medical faculty; and in the dispensary we note a particularly creditable feature of the establishment. Mr. Farnworth has rightly recognised in this the most important and responsible division of his business, and he pays the closest attention to the faithful performance of all duties incidental to it. Every prescription is registered in full; and by this means a reference and an exact copy are always obtainable, no matter how remote the date may be. The compounding of prescriptions is accomplished with the utmost punctuality and despatch consistent with accuracy; and the drugs, chemicals, and pharmaceutical preparations used are all of a character whose purity can be conscientiously guaranteed, everything being of the first quality exclusively. All new remedies are prepared or procured as soon as introduced into reputable practice, and medicines are forwarded to all parts of the country with the least possible delay. In this latter connection we may mention that prescriptions are sent in to Mr. Farnworth from great distances to be made up; and in Wales, for instance, the house has a large *clientèle* among the county families, some of whom take the advice of their London physician, but send his prescriptions to be prepared at this well-known and reliable pharmacy. In the manufacture of carbonated waters, which he commenced and carried on in conjunction with the pharmacy shortly after the establishment of the latter, Mr. Farnworth has developed a very notable department. It was with the primary object of producing an article of superior quality that he entered upon this line of business, and so greatly have his endeavours in this

direction been recognised that his table waters receive the patronage of the nobility, aristocracy, and gentry in this and other parts of the kingdom; were supplied at the luncheon on the occasion of the recent visit of the Prince and Princess of Wales to this town, and were, we believe, partaken of by her Royal Highness, and several of the nobility then present. His preparations include soda, potass, seltzer, and lithia waters, ginger ale, and lemonade, which are put up in half-pint and quarter-pint bottles, and also in syphons; and these beverages have won a splendid reputation for absolute purity and palatable quality. They are manufactured with the utmost care from the very best ingredients; and we believe that Mr. Farnworth is the oldest producer of these waters in the Blackburn district. In all its characteristics the business here briefly reviewed is a credit to its proprietor and to the town in which it is so well known. The stock at the pharmacy is maintained in admirable order and condition; and Mr. Farnworth has a staff of thoroughly competent assistants, who have long been in his service—one for twenty-five and one for fifteen years. The business is thus under the most competent management and direction, and the house stands in a position to satisfy every pharmaceutical requirement. The proprietor is a gentleman of very high attainments in his profession, and the methods and principles which have always marked his administration of the establishment have secured the approval and won the full confidence of a widespread and distinguished patronage.

William Jackson, Consulting Engineer, 36, Penny Street, Blackburn.—In all businesses, trades, and professions, after the first rudiments have been acquired, it is experience that makes the specialist, and such has been the case with Mr. William Jackson, of 36, Penny Street, Blackburn, who commenced business in 1886 as a consulting engineer, after having gained a vast amount of practical experience with the eminent firm of engineers, Messrs. W. & J. Yates, of Blackburn, with whom Mr. Jackson was associated for over twenty years. In turning his engineering knowledge to practical and profitable account, Mr. Jackson undertakes the making of plans for engines, boilers, mills and sheds, and the levelling, lining, and squaring of engines and shafts. He gives estimates for examining, indicating, and reporting the condition of engines, making his reports monthly or quarterly as arranged, and through his long experience in the erection of engines and boilers he has every confidence that he will give satisfaction. Mr. Jackson is agent for a number of the accessories of engines and boilers, and, among others, he acts for Messrs. Hopkinson & Co. for their patent parallel slide valves, in diameters from $\frac{1}{2}$ inch up to 2 inches. He also undertakes the repair of Hopkinson's high pressure and low water safety valves. He retains in his premises a varied stock of wrought iron steam and gas-tubing, brass and iron steam taps, glands and gasfittings, rubber washers, and asbestos packing; and he has fitted up the newest and best types of machinery for cutting and screwing, and is prepared to fit up mills and all classes of works and factories on the most approved principles. He gives in his estimates with great moderation of charges, and he has already secured a splendid connection with the millowners, bleachers, printers and dyers all over this district of Lancashire. The work undertaken by Mr. Jackson is always executed by thoroughly trained workmen and done under his own personal supervision, and he is thus enabled to guarantee thoroughness, both in material and construction.

Edward Mercer, Boot and Shoe Manufacturer, 46, Darwen Street, Blackburn.—Mr. Edward Mercer commenced this business in 1874, and now possesses a most extensive connection in that line of trade in the district. His premises comprise a very commodious shop, with workroom to the rear. The sale shop is divided by a counter running parallel to the show window, and behind that is a fitting room specially for ladies. An improved alteration was made on the premises two years ago, giving a better appearance to the frontage, which is now one of the handsomest shops in Blackburn connected with the boot and shoe trade, while the interior fittings are exceptionally good. About a dozen men are in constant employment on the premises, and bespoke work of every description, including riding, shooting, military, and gentlemen's patent and dress boots and shoes, also Russian leather boots and shoes of every colour and description, receives most careful and prompt attention; the above being made on the hand-sewn principle and in the most substantial manner. Fifteen hundred pairs of bespoke, and five thousand pairs of repairs passed through the work-shops of the above establishment, which ranks as one of the best in Lancashire, between July 1st, 1888, and June 30th, 1889. The stock of goods embrace every description of boot, shoe, and slipper, and are all of a very superior order; but the proprietor makes a speciality in football boots, in the making of which he is unequalled in the United Kingdom. The great success which has attended his efforts in supplying a first-class football boot is evidenced by the fact that he is now supplying all the principal clubs and players in England and Scotland, from whom he has received the highest testimonials, a very particular feature being that he supplies clubs and individual players at the one uniform rate of eleven shillings and sixpence per pair, the superior qualities of these boots being lightness, strength, fit, and durability. Mr. Mercer conducts his business on most approved lines, and civility and attention are marked features on the part of his assistants. He is very popular with his patrons, and much respected by the public generally.

Lithographic and Fine Art Printing Works, Mill Lane, Blackburn; Engraving Works, Preston New Road.—In connection with the printing and engraving industries a well-known firm in Blackburn of old standing which deserves honourable mention in these reviews is that of R. Dugdale & Son, of Mill Lane Engraving Works, 36, Preston New Road. This business was established as far back as the year 1826 by Mr. Richard Dugdale, who died in 1874, after which the business was successfully carried on by his son, who died in 1881. Since then the business has been conducted by the latter's widow, under the able superintendence of her son, Richard, who is a grandson of the founder. Mill Lane Printing Works occupy the two upper floors of a large building of three storeys in height, and are equipped in first-class style with all the most approved modern machinery, including three lithographic machines by Greaves, which were awarded the gold medal at the Liverpool Exhibition of 1887; five presses by Furnival, of Manchester; bookbinding and other special machines and appliances by the foremost makers, all of which are driven by a powerful "Otto" gas engine. For many years this firm has occupied a position in the front ranks of the trade, and at present the house is entrusted with the most important engraving and lithographic work for the most influential houses in and around Blackburn. Amongst the latest important work executed by this firm worthy of notice four million lithographic pictures for Lever's celebrated "Sunlight Soap," some of which our readers probably have seen somewhere; a "transparent illumination" of Blackburn Town Hall, in honour of her Majesty's Jubilee, a copy of which was accepted by the Queen. The production of this beautiful picture, it should be mentioned, won great praise to the house, as such a work was never known to be produced by any other firm in the United Kingdom; and although amply repaid, the trouble in executing it and the expense were enormous. It should also be mentioned that this firm has executed the "foundation plates" for every public building in Blackburn, and have still the honour of being entrusted with this important work. The trade of the firm, in which a large number of highly skilled hands are employed, extends all over Blackburn and into the surrounding districts, a large business being done in "zinco etching," which forms one of the specialities of the house. The proprietress of the business is an agreeable, courteous lady, and her son, Mr. Richard Dugdale, conducts the business in a manner which displays the same artistic taste and practical skill in all departments that have characterised the management of the business since it was founded sixty-two years ago, and through which the old-established reputation of the firm continues to be maintained and extended.

Johnson & Co., Mineral Water Manufacturers, St. Peter's Street, Blackburn.—Messrs. Johnson & Co. are among the best known and oldest established firms of mineral water manufacturers in Blackburn and district. The premises are situated in St. Peter's Street, and have been in existence for nearly half a century. The works were originally established for the manufacture of mineral waters by Mr. William Carr, in the year 1842. This gentleman only retired from the concern in the year 1883, when he was succeeded by the present proprietors, trading as Messrs. Johnson & Co. These large works possess all the necessary plant, of the very latest and most approved designs, for the manufacture of all the popular mineral waters at present so much in demand, as well as the machinery for the brewing of hop beer and stout. Some of these excellent machines are supplied by the well-known firms of Galloway of Bolton, mineral water machine manufacturers, McEwen, Hayward, and Messrs. Taylor & Co., all of which names are ample evidence of the first-class character of the goods supplied by them. There is a very extensive output, as the demand for the produce of the firm is exceedingly large and is always increasing, although the trade is almost confined to the town of Blackburn and the large district surrounding it. Messrs. Johnson & Co. have had a long and extensive experience in the business, and every department of the concern is under the careful personal management and superintendence of the proprietors, so that customers may depend upon the quality of the goods being kept up to the highest and most satisfactory standard of excellence.

James Birtwell, Wholesale Grocer, &c., Mincing Lane, Blackburn.—This important firm commenced business in 1872 in Market Street, and in 1877 was removed to Mincing Lane, where he has succeeded in establishing an excellent and prosperous connection, extending over a considerably wide area. The premises in Mincing Lane comprise a commodious office and warehouses, and consist of a large building thirty feet by fifty-four, and three storeys high, with large cellarage. The whole of this large space is used for stock and for packing up orders. A very heavy stock of grocery goods of all kinds is always on hand, with a very large assortment of butter and other provisions of all kinds, of the first quality, and from the very best markets. A very large business is done, about half a dozen men being always employed on the premises, while a couple of travellers are always "on the road," representing the firm. The trade is chiefly confined to Lancashire alone, but the volume of business is exceedingly large, as the firm enjoys one of the highest reputations in the wholesale trade. Mr. Birtwell has already had thirty years' experience in the business, and the whole concern is under his personal care and superintendence, and he displays the greatest amount of enterprise and energy in its administration. He is held in the highest respect by his fellow townsmen, and is especially esteemed by the commercial and trading community.

Robert Thomas Eastwood, Flagger and Slater, Victoria Flag and Slate Yard, Regent Street, Blackburn.—This business, which is one of the foremost of its kind in Lancashire, was established at the present address in the year 1881 by Mr. Eastwood, who is still the sole proprietor. The yard is of large extent, being about 100 feet square. The buildings upon it comprise an office and spacious stores, the latter being used for keeping cements of every kind, hair for plaster work, mortar, laths, nails, &c., and the yard is stocked with flags of every description, including Yorkshire, Darwen, and Cunliff flags, for which Mr. Eastwood is the agent in Blackburn, as well as an immense stock of sanitary pipes, chimney-tops, stones, slates, and other building materials. The trade of the firm, in which there are sometimes as many as one hundred men employed, extends all over Lancashire and Yorkshire, a large business being done in the sale of stones, flags, slates, and all kinds of building material. Mr. Eastwood's business connection is of the most influential order, and has been formed by hard working, a thorough practical knowledge of every detail of the trade, and honourable methods in the management of his business, which have won for him a high place in the esteem and confidence of both buyer and seller. Mr. Robert T. Eastwood, who began life, with no adventitious aid from fortune, commenced business for himself in 1878, and the same energy and perseverance which had hitherto been devoted to his employers was now applied to his own business, with the result that after three years' trading he had to seek larger premises than those he at first occupied, and in 1881 he removed to his present commodious establishment in Regent Street. So well has the business been conducted that at the present time Mr. Eastwood is one of the leading men of his native town in his own trade, several large and important building contracts having been entrusted to him, and executed with entire satisfaction. He is also vice-president of the Master Builders' Association. From the *Oddfellows' Magazine* of January last we learn that Mr. Eastwood first became acquainted with Oddfellowship in 1873, when he was initiated a member of the "Commercial" Lodge, and his knowledge of figures was so well known that he was immediately appointed auditor of the lodge accounts. He was not long in passing the various subordinate offices of his lodge, as in 1878 he was appointed N.G., and in 1879, Lodge Grand Master. His valuable work in connection with the Order was not allowed to pass unrecognised, as in 1877 he was presented with a pair of framed emblems, and at the expiration of his term as G.M. of the Lodge, he received in May, 1880, a handsome marble clock in recognition of the exceptional services he had rendered. In the December following he was appointed Deputy Grand Master of the Blackburn District, and the next year was unanimously elected Prov. G.M. In that year the Jubilee of the District was celebrated by a banquet at the Old Bull Hotel, which was presided over by Alderman Lund, the mayor of the town, and was attended by several P.G.M.s of the Order. A considerable share in the arrangements for these festivities, which proved most successful, naturally fell on the shoulders of Brother Eastwood. No surprise, therefore, need be exhibited at his appointment as Trustee of the District in 1882. Southport A.M.C. in 1881 saw in him the representative of the Blackburn District, and the A.M.C. meetings of 1882 and 1883 at Cardiff and Nottingham respectively were visited by Brother Eastwood in his representative capacity, as also those of the next two years at Reading and Aberystwith. At the last-named gathering he first obtained a seat at the Board of Directors, which he retained until 1887, when at Dover he was elected Deputy Grand Master of the Order; and at Gloucester in 1888 he was elected to the distinguished position of Grand Master of the Order. Among his other services to the Blackburn District may be stated his vigorous advocacy of measures of financial reform, which we are pleased to know have on his recommendation been adopted. The result has been that the entire district is now solvent, and more, for it possesses a surplus of £11,000. It should also be mentioned that Blackburn had on his appointment as a Director shown, by entertaining Mr. Eastwood at a complimentary banquet, that it was not unmindful of the honour brought to it by one of its members. The banquet was presided over by Alderman Whiteley, the then mayor, who was supported by Sir Robert Peel, Bart., M.P., the officers of the Order, and the whole of his colleagues on the Directory. Outside the Order Mr. Eastwood has been almost as active as within its pale. For many years he was a sidesman of St. Michael's Church, is a trustee of the Third Blackburn Starr-Bowkett Building Society, is a member of "Perseverance Lodge" No. 345 of Free and Accepted Masons, one of the managers of the Higher Grade School, and is connected by various positions with a large number of other different societies. In 1881 he was brought forward as a candidate for the representation of Trinity Ward in the Town Council, and was returned without opposition, which was repeated in 1884, and again in 1887. He is claimed as a member on the Watch, Water, Highway, Health, Scavenging, Town Hall and Public Baths Committees, and of nearly all the sub-committees. His undoubtedly valuable services in connection with the Town Hall and Public Baths Committee were to some extent recognised in April, 1884, when he had the honour of opening the new first-class baths, and in commemoration of that event was presented with a gold key. After the ceremony he entertained the Mayor and Corporation to a banquet, and in the somewhat novel situation of the bottom of the second-class plunge-bath! He was one of the Reception Committee on the occasion of the recent Royal visit to Blackburn, and had the honour of being presented, with other members of the committee, to H.R.H. the Prince of Wales.

Henry Shaw & Co., Salford New Brewery, Blackburn. —The largely recognised concern carried on by Messrs. Henry Shaw & Co., ale and porter brewers, malsters, and dealers in hops, at the Salford New Brewery, Blackburn, was established on the existing site in the year 1834 by Mr. Henry Shaw. A few years later Mr. John Rutherford was introduced into the business; the title then became Henry Shaw & Co. The sons of these men—also named Henry Shaw and John Rutherford—now conduct the concern. Mr. John Rutherford is the present mayor of

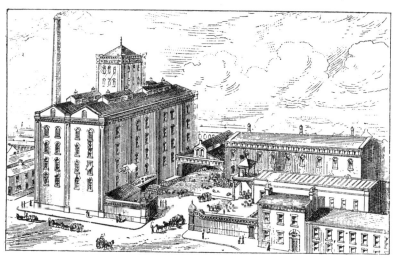

Blackburn. The brewery was rebuilt in the year 1868, and now comprises a handsome range of buildings in brick and freestone. It is erected on the tower system, this large tower of sixty feet square rising to a height of eight floors. The premises are fitted with a hoist for lifting the grain from the ground to the top storey, an excellent convenience for the saving of both time and labour. The plant is entirely of the best and most modern description. The business here is entirely for home consumption, an excellent trade being conducted in bitter and mild ales and porter. The firm do all their own malting, and have also very extensive transactions in hops. A suite of stables adjoins the brewery. The

Salford New Brewery affords employment to a considerable working staff of hands.. A fine range of the firm's public and private offices adjoin the brewery, and the firm have a connection of a large number of "tied" houses. This business is in the hands of men of thorough probity and energy, and among the various business concerns of the county there are few in a position to lay claim to a larger share of public esteem and confidence than are Messrs. Henry Shaw and Co. of the Salford New Brewery, Blackburn.

Clayton, Goodfellow & Co., Engineers, Millwrights, Iron and Brass Founders, &c., Atlas Iron Works, Darwen Street, Blackburn.—This business was established in the year 1850 in the present premises by Messrs. Clayton & Goodfellow, the designation of the firm being changed to Clayton, Goodfellow & Co. some fourteen years ago. The present partnership consists of Messrs. John Harrison, William Loynd, and R. H. Clayton. The Atlas Iron Works occupy an area of 5,000 square yards, and employ a working staff of about three hundred hands. The premises comprise the foundry, moulding shop and machinery department. Messrs. Clayton, Goodfellow & Co. are makers of all kinds of portable and stationary compound engines, boiler mountings and valves, printing and calendering machinery; as also machinery for grinding mills of every description, hydraulic presses, &c. A speciality with Messrs. Clayton, Goodfellow & Co. is the production of steel piston and bucket springs, made on what is known as Goodfellow's principle. These springs are remarkable for their lightness, elasticity, and durability, and are supplied by the firm to existing pistons and air pump buckets of their own make, new pistons and buckets complete, fitted with these springs, being supplied on the shortest notice. Messrs. Clayton, Goodfellow & Co. are largely engaged in the manufacture of beams, pillars, and gutters, cranes, lifting crabs, screw jacks, bevel, spur, mitre, and bevel wheels, also machine-moulded cog-wheel castings, with any size, form, or breadth of cogs; drums for ropes or belts are made and turned by machinery to any diameter up to 30 feet, or width up to 5 feet, and plans and specifications submitted for the erection of new works. The firm make no charge in any case for pattern-making for machine-made wheels; and some idea of the popularity of their manufactures may be inferred from the fact that Messrs. Clayton, Goodfellow & Co. have made upwards of ten thousand patent metallic pistons and air-pump buckets. This firm conduct a most extensive home and foreign trade, and have at present large orders on hand for India, Mexico, Portugal, &c., and it goes without saying that in every department of their business the partners of Messrs. Clayton, Goodfellow & Co., of the Atlas Iron Works, Blackburn, are men of not only sound technical skill and experience, but also of the most praiseworthy perseverance and probity. This firm are connected by telephone to the principal towns and works of Lancashire; telephone 27.

Cookson & Clegg, Curriers and Leather Dressers, Mincing Lane, Blackburn.—Established in the year 1860, this business has been carried on by Mr. Clegg since the death of his partner which took place in 1878. The premises are of large extent, occupying a building of four storeys in height, and measuring sixty by forty feet at the base. They consist of a large front shop on the ground floor, with warehouse in the rear; boot upper manufactory on the floor above leather shaving and splitting department on the third floor; and drying-room with currying workshop on the fourth. The trade of the firm, in which a large staff of hands are employed, extends all over Lancashire, a large wholesale business being done with boot and shoe manufacturers and public works, the latter being large buyers of the house's products in leather belting and other forms of leather, such as laces, picking bands, butts, &c. Mr. Clegg is a well-known gentleman, and possessing an agreeable obliging manner and a reputation for the honourable methods that have characterised the management of his business since it was founded about thirty years ago, he enjoys a high place in the esteem and confidence of all who meet him, whether in connection with business or matters of public interest.

Thomas Winter & Co., Engineers, Machinists, and Makers of Sizing Apparatus, Brass and Ironfounders, Perseverance Brass and Copper Works, Byrom Street and Canterbury Street, Blackburn.—This thoroughly representative house was established in the year 1875 by its present principal, Mr. Thomas Winter, who commenced busi-

ness in St. Peter Street, Blackburn, and removed thence to the address now occupied in 1888. This removal was necessitated by the large proportions the business had attained, its growth and development having been continuous from the very first under Mr. Winter's energetic management. The Perseverance Brass and Copper Works cover an area of 1,035 square yards, and have good frontages to Byrom Street and

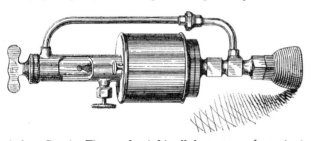

Canterbury Street. They are devoted to all the purposes of a most extensive and comprehensive industry, the productions of which include steam engines, hydraulic presses, sizing apparatus, brass and iron pumps, ginger-beer machines, bottling machines, lathes, patent slack strap hoists, patent heating apparatus, drilling machines, valves of all kinds, water and steam gauges, compound lubricators, steam whistles, gas, steam and water-cocks of every kind, hand and stand pipes, hydrants, hose couplings, and every

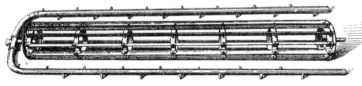

description of large and small brass and copper work. The staff employed is numerous and highly efficient; the workshops contain a very complete outfit of the best modern machinery; and the house enjoys a splendid reputation for the quality and finished character of its productions. Specialities of importance have been developed in brass and copper apparatus for brewers' use, also in warp reels, yarn testers, patent immersion skeleton

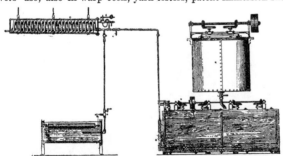

rollers, and perforated copper boiling tubes for bleaching, dyeing, sizing, &c. Another notable production is Messrs. Winter's patent sight-feed lubricator, for high or low pressure steam engines. These are being produced in great numbers, the many advantages of the invention being fully recognised by steam users. One of these advantages is that there is no pres-

sure on the cup, and the necessity of continual emptying is thus obviated. Again, there is no pressure in the glass, a great improvement on the old system, which caused so many breakages; and, finally, there is but one connection with the cylinder. This sight-feed lubricator certainly meets a long-existent requirement, and the merits of the patent are fully attested by the favour it has obtained in practical quarters. Messrs. Winter have recently completed an important work in putting a water engine into St. Peter's Church, Blackburn, to feed the bellows of the fine organ in use in that edifice. A great feature in connection with this engine is a double automatic pump, by which both bellows can be filled at the same time. The difficulty, hitherto, has consisted in the fact that when one of the bellows was filled before the other, the action of the pump was stopped. Many noted organ builders have said that this difficulty could not be overcome; but Messrs. Winter & Co. have very effectually conquered it by means of an escape lever, which allows the pump to work continuously. The water engine in St. Peter's Church is thus an emphatic and thoroughly practical success, and is one of the best achievements of this firm in hydraulic engineering—a branch of industry and mechanics with which their name is very creditably identified in many ways. Messrs. Winter have also introduced an improved arrangement for sizing coloured yarns separately from the grey. The difficulty in running the two yarns evenly together has been overcome by Messrs. Winter by a change of wheels, which can be altered to run faster or slower, so slightly as to make only 1 inch in 500, or 1 inch in 1,000. The arrangement is so simple that it can be changed in a few seconds by any unskilled workman. This avoids the turning of both copper rollers, as under the old system, as by this method any diameters of rollers can be worked accurately together, delivering the yarns with the same tension. T. Winter & Co. are sole makers of a machine for steeping pickers by Green's process, obviating the three months' soaking in oil necessary under the old system. Messrs. Winter & Co.'s business has grown continuously from the first, and its valuable connections are still increasing. The trade operations of the firm extend all over the United Kingdom, and are beginning to take very influential effect abroad, notably in Russia, India, and the Colonies. The house gives promise of great future prosperity and distinction, and Mr. Winter's able management and practical supervision afford a strong assurance that this promise will be fulfilled.

Rowland Baguley & Co., Shuttle Manufacturers, Addison Road, Blackburn.—This business dates back in its foundation to the year 1840, having been established at Manchester, but Mr. Baguley, wisely discerning the importance of Blackburn as a rising centre of the cotton-weaving industry, removed to this town about the year 1854, and took part of the Eagle Foundry, and after the explosion there, located the business in George Street West, where it was most successfully carried on until 1878, when, in consequence of its increasing development and the necessity for further accommodation, the present extensive and commodious premises in Addison Street were acquired. These, however, have been enlarged to meet the growing demands of the trade to nearly double their original size, and now constitute one of the largest establishments of their kind in the kingdom. The main buildings for storage purposes are of two storeys, the working parts being admirably constructed and well arranged, with single storey and lighted from the top. The various departments are replete with the most modern machinery and appliances, embodying all the latest improvements and the most comprehensive utilities. The workshops are situated on the ground floors, the upper floors are stocked with enormous quantities of cut blocks of fine-grained boxwood in course of seasoning, and valued at several thousand pounds. In boxwood nothing but fine selected Persian or from the Caucasus mountain district being used, the boxwood known as West Indian, which is of a cheaper but very inferior kind, being entirely discarded by this firm. The stock of cut-up shuttle blocks kept in stock are always sufficient to keep the works eighteen months without a supply of wood or log being obtained. Owing to the death of Mr. Baguley and his son, the business is now the property of Mr. Duckworth, son-in-law to Mr. Baguley, who for some years had the management of the concern. Some idea of the magnitude of the operations here carried out may be gathered from the fact that the firm turn out 4,000 to 5,000 shuttles per week, suitable for calico and fine wool weaving. Upwards of fifty men and boys being regularly employed, the works at all times present a busy and animated scene of industrial activity. Messrs. R. Baguley & Co. have a splendid business connection, the home trade extending to all parts of the United Kingdom, and the export business to the Continent of Europe, India, Japan, America North and South, and in fact to all parts of the civilized world wherever these indispensable adjuncts to weaving operations are in use. The firm have introduced many inventions and improvements in the construction of the shuttle, with which their name has long been associated. The business in every department is under direct and careful supervision, and the operations are conducted with that energy and enterprise which have always so strongly animated this firm. The firm is represented on the Manchester Exchange every Tuesday, and is to be found at No. 12 Arch.

Blackburn Supply Stores, 31, Preston New Road, Blackburn.—In connection with the provision industry a well-known establishment, which deserves honourable mention in these reviews, is the Blackburn Supply Stores, now so popular for its malt, wheat meal, and Scotch confectionery, and which is situated at 31, Preston New Road. The Blackburn Supply Stores and Bakery are of large extent, the former occupying a handsome building of three storeys in height in the front, the bakery being in a separate building behind. With large plate-glass windows and tastefully fitted up inside, the sale-shop has a most attractive appearance from the street, displaying an admirably arranged stock of high-class groceries, provisions, and such goods as are found in a London Italian

Whitehead. B'burn.

warehouse of the first order. The two floors above the sale-shop are used as warehouses, and are stocked with the various classes of goods displayed below. Equipped in first-class style with all the most approved appliances, the bakery is admirably suited to meet the increasing demands for its famous products, in which especially malt bread, wheat meal, and Scotch confectionery the house does an enormous business. Blackburn Supply Stores having won a high reputation for the excellence of the goods dealt in in every department enjoys the confidence of a very large and increasing number of firm supporters. They were opened in the year 1886, under the supervision of Mr. James Cockbain, the present manager, to whose energy, experience, and agreeable courteous manner the popularity of these stores is largely due. But doubtless the facilities enjoyed by the house for buying large quantities of goods in the foremost markets on terms that enable them to place their high-class goods within the reach of all classes, by charging wholesale prices, is the chief secret of this firm's success.

Crook & Hewitt, Timber Merchants, &c., Fish Lane Saw Mills, Blackburn.—This business is one of considerable standing, both in respect to the influential character of the connection, and also as regards the length of its career, having been founded in 1850 by the late Mr. John Kershaw. In 1885 it came into the hands of Messrs. Crook & Hewitt, and under their able and energetic direction the reputation of the establishment is not only being maintained, but is being extended to all parts of the locality. The Fish Lane Saw Mills cover a considerable area, and embrace the usual departments that are incidental to establishments where timber of all kinds is dealt with in view of its use for different purposes. The firm supply every description of timber, the stock consisting of a good selection of logs, deals, and boards, also a large variety of sawn and seasoned wood cut to different thicknesses and sizes, including veneer and fancy woods. A large amount of work is done in sawing, the mills being equipped with wood-cutting machinery, also fret-sawing, a speciality of the house. Wood-turning is also an important department, the works being replete with all the necessary plant incidental thereto. In every branch of the business the work is executed in a thoroughly satisfactory manner, all kinds of orders being executed with commendable promptitude, and the management throughout conducted on sound commercial principles.

R. Denham, Wholesale Bookseller, Stationer, Printer, Bookbinder, &c., North-east Lancashire Educational Depôt, King William Street, Blackburn.—This business was founded at Market House, thirty years ago, by Mr. Denham, who has occupied his present premises for the last twelve years. The establishment is of large extent, tastefully fitted up, and displays to advantage a valuable stock of books and stationery. Besides novels, scientific, tradesmen's, and books belonging to stationery, such as account books, ledgers, &c., this house does a very large trade in educational books, of which there is a complete stock displayed in the handsome warehouse. The trade extends over north-east Lancashire. Mr. Denham is well known and much respected in the trade.

Hill Brothers, Silk Mercers and General Drapers, 21, King William Street, Blackburn.—This well-known house was founded at this address in 1883, the present sole proprietor being Mr. W. G. Hill. The stock held is large, well selected, and of the best and finest quality, while a leading speciality of the house for which the firm has a high reputation is the manufacture of costumes and millinery of every description. Over the spacious double-fronted shop are situated commodious showrooms, and over the showrooms are large workrooms, where many hands are employed regularly in this branch of industry. In black and coloured silks of all kinds they make an excellent display, and their finished costumes are "perfection," imparting a trim and *svelte* appearance to all wearers; and there is also a large assortment of satins, velvets, and French and English dress goods generally. In drapery they also hold an immense stock of Nottingham lace curtains, which we understand they obtain direct from the Nottingham looms, the quality of which can be guaranteed, together with ginghams, checks, calicoes, and art muslins, and such like besides too numerous to mention. They show novel yet inexpensive bonnets, which when seen, it must be confessed, are of the most *recherché* description. And, again, here and there, are to be found shapes of all kinds, and ribbons of every shade and hue; in fact all the materials are kept in stock which will enable amateur milliners to put together at small cost a hat or bonnet that shall not betray its home-spun origin. Another very important and well represented department is that for furs, which are bought direct in every new shape or colour that is produced. The business is well organised, and the whole of the stock kept in excellent order, inasmuch that mourning orders and all other commands placed with the house can be executed in a few hours to the entire satisfaction of customers. We must not omit to mention the huge stock of newest and most fashionable dressmakers' trimmings for which the house is so justly famed. The trade is of a good medium class, and well established in the town and neighbourhood.

John Haworth, Borough Wire Works, Mincing Lane, Blackburn.—In connection with the important industry of the wire-worker and the trade of the ironmonger, a well-known firm of old standing which deserves honourable mention in these reviews is that of John Haworth, of the Borough Wire Works, Mincing Lane, Blackburn. This business, which is the foremost of its kind in this district of Lancashire, was founded in the year 1835 by Francis Anderton, who was succeeded by Alfred Waterworth, and lastly by Mr. John Haworth, the present proprietor, who has owned the business for the past twelve years. Borough Wire Works cover a large area of ground, and consist of a building of three storeys in height, which is divided into weaving work on the upper floor, wire-cloth warehouse on the floor below, and show-room, with offices on the ground flat. The looms in the weaving work produce wire-netting for sheep, game, aviaries, &c.; strong iron wove wire for mining purposes; gauze wire for steam joints, safety lamps, blinds, &c., the meshes ranging from 16 to 120 in the inch. Of these wire cloths a valuable stock is displayed in the firm's large warehouse and show-room, as well as a great variety of other goods, such as strained wire fencing, meat safes and dish covers, fenders and fire-guards, poultry

fences, wire staples, riddles, sieves, sand screens, window guards, &c. In addition to these classes of goods belonging to wire-working and wire-weaving, the warehouse and show-room exhibits a large selection of garden implements, including garden arches, flower stands, garden seats and chairs, pea and strawberry guards, lawn mowers, garden rolls, hose reels, garden engines, &c., wire and venetian blinds. As iron, tinplate, wire and metal merchants, this house also keeps in stock all kinds of sheet and rod iron, galvanised sheet iron, galvanised corrugated roofing sheets, iron, brass, and copper wire, perforated and sheet zinc, perforated and sheet copper, sheet brass, tin plates, &c. The trade of the firm is very extensive, requiring the services of fourteen assistants, and the business connection, which is of the most influential order, extends over Lancashire and Yorkshire, a considerable export trade being also done with Rotterdam, Australia, &c. Mr. Haworth, the proprietor of this important concern, is a well-known gentleman, and on account of his agreeable, courteous manner and the honourable methods that characterise the management of his business he is much liked and highly respected by his numerous influential supporters, and all with whom he comes in contact, whether in connection with business or matters affecting the public interests.

Daniel Thwaites & Co., Eanam Brewery, Blackburn.— This successful business was established in 1807 by Messrs. Duckworth & Clayton, the firm afterwards becoming Messrs. Duckworth, Clayton, & Thwaites, and at a later period being known under the title of Messrs. Thomas, Daniel, & John Thwaites. In 1858 the concern was taken over by Mr. Daniel Thwaites, and has since been continued by that gentleman. Mr. Thwaites commenced operations with an output of seven thousand barrels (of thirty-six gallons) per annum. As indicating the business progress achieved by this gentleman, however, it may be stated that the output of the Eanam Brewery now reaches seventy thousand barrels per annum. The brewery covers an area of nearly two acres of ground, and employs a staff of about a hundred hands. It has been fitted up with the most approved and modern appliances in plant, &c. This firm enjoy a widespread and special celebrity on account of their brewing of heavy mild ales. The original founder of the business, Mr. Thwaites, died in 1888, and the concern has since been conducted under the title of Daniel Thwaites & Co., with all that energy and strict business promptitude which characterised its original proprietors.

W. Butterfield, M.P.S., Chemist and Wholesale Druggist, Nova Scotia, Blackburn.—In reviewing the leading houses engaged in connection with the operations of chemists, drysalters, &c. in the locality of Blackburn, special reference must be made to the business that is carried on by Mr. William Butterfield at the above address. It has long been well known, not only among the general public, but also in the trade, having been founded as far back as 1863, when it was located in premises on the opposite side of the thoroughfare to that in which it is now situated. The present premises are of considerable extent, and include a large shop, elegantly fitted and heavily stocked with a choice assortment of the purest drugs and chemicals of all kinds and descriptions. A noticeable feature is the elegant window display, which is one of the most artistically arranged and effective to be met with in this district. The whole of the fittings are throughout of the highest order. The premises are admirably arranged, and there are few establishments that present such an elegant and highly attractive appearance. Mr. Butterfield conducts a large retail trade in all the usual branches that are incidental to a chemist's business, and he also commands a very extensive wholesale trade in all kinds of drugs and drysalter's goods. He is widely renowned in connection with the preparation of various specifics, remedies, &c., among the principal of which are the celebrated Cough Linctus, which has met with great success, and the Champion baking powder. A striking speciality of the trade is to be found in Butterfield's Children's Teething Powders, which save many a heavy doctor's bill. They are spoken of as the mother's comfort, and are immensely popular far and wide. Butterfield's renowned syrup is acknowledged by thousands (in Blackburn alone) to be one of the best, safest, and most effectual medicines that can be given to infants and young children. This speciality alone has a most extensive demand, which proves beyond the shadow of a doubt the beneficial qualities of this celebrated syrup. In all these, and in other specialities, too numerous to mention, the trade extends not only throughout the locality adjacent to the establishment, but also generally in all parts of the north of England, the firm being represented by able travellers. A large trade is also done in teas, coffees, spices, vinegars, sauces, cigars, and snuffs, oils, colours, varnishes, and dye-wares, in all of which the proprietor deals extensively, and keeps a large and varied stock. Connected with the principal portion of the premises there are spacious stores, in which the goods above indicated are kept in large quantities, and in every department the proprietor maintains a high standard of quality, supplying only the best class of goods that can be obtained. The stable, delivery float, van, well-bred and spirited horses used in this important business all go to testify to the energy, spirit, pluck, and perseverance displayed in the management on the part of the worthy and enterprising proprietor.

John Myers, Brush Manufacturer, Bridge End House, Church Street, Blackburn.—An old and worthy house in the brush-making industry is that of the gentleman whose name appears at the head of this notice, the business having been founded by him at premises in Northgate over half a century ago, the occupancy of the warehouse and factory now used dating from 1880. The shop is capacious, lofty, and well appointed, being chiefly utilised as a stock-room, in which brushes of all kinds are packed from floor to ceiling. On the floors above the shop and adjoining premises is the brush factory, where a full staff of experienced hands are employed regularly in this staple branch of British industry. The operations of the house are chiefly confined to what is technically known as hair-brushes, though it does not imply that only brushes used for the dressing of the hair are here made, but those in which *bonâ-fide* hair is used, and not fibre. In this line every description of brush usually manufactured is here found, substantially put together and finished in the best possible manner. It is undoubtedly a fact that the high repute the house has attained throughout the trade is due to the truism that every item in stock will stand the strictest scrutiny, in proof that the merits of the various brushes displayed and their general design are of no mean order and all that could be desired. About twenty-five years ago Mr. Myers introduced a broom for mill use, which is a combination of Brazil weed and bristles. It is called the "Nelson" broom, and will last the time of three of the ordinary class. It is largely used, and has attained great success by reason of mill sweeping being more effectually accomplished and at a greatly reduced cost by this broom than by other kinds. For many years this old house has done a very large trade, and it is evident that Mr. Myers keeps his stock well abreast of the times, for he has all the facilities for making all kinds of brushes, and that too by the most improved method; while the organisation of the business is so complete that the largest shipping order imaginable can be executed at a few hours' notice. The trade is almost entirely wholesale, and well established. The proprietor is a gentleman of great enterprise and business ability, and held in high esteem by all with whom he has commercial relations.

James Boyle & Co., Wholesale Confectioners, &c., Blackburn.—This concern was established in 1822 by Alderman James Boyle, in Salford, and removed to the present premises in the year 1866. At this date the three sons of the founder of the business, Messrs. William, James, and Robert Boyle, were introduced into partnership, and shortly afterwards, William Boyle, Esq., was created a justice of the peace, and retired from the business about ten years ago. Since that date the concern has been conducted by Messrs. James and Robert Boyle, under its present title of James Boyle and Co. These works reach to a height of three storeys, and are built in brick, and cover an area of two thousand square yards, a staff of one hundred hands being employed. The premises comprise the following departments : offices, fruit-preserving and marmalade-making sections, boiling-room, and pan goods and fancy confectionery. On the first storey is the boiling department, bakeries, and offices, the second floor being allocated to the departments of lozenge manufacture and storage. The third storey is set apart for the work connected with storage, making up, and packing ; and all the departments are suit-

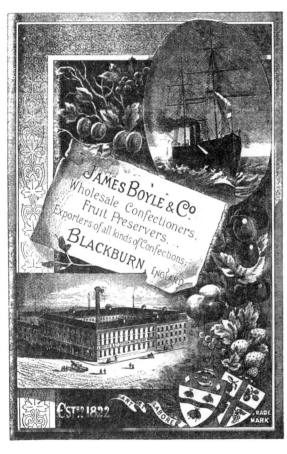

ably fitted out for the work engaged in. The entire fruit pulp is kept in special fireproof stores situated at Watson's buildings. The machinery employed by Messrs. James Boyle & Co. is of the best construction, and embraces cutting, rolling, shaping, and finishing machines, and meat pie-making and dropping appliances, the whole being driven by an engine of thirty horse-power. The boiler is of immense capacity, owing to the large amount of steam required by the firm for general purposes. The retail department of this business is situated in Victoria Street, and consists of a single-fronted shop, measuring about ten square yards, fitted with large plate-glass window and possessing a handsome frontal of some thirty feet. The works contain a very large stock of all kinds of sweets boiled and dried, jams, preserves, marmalades, and fancy confectionery. This firm is of a distinctly leading class in Blackburn, engaging several commercial travellers, and enjoying a trade not only extensive and widespread, but conducted on the most energetic, systematic, and honourable principles.

John Hayes, Rope Manufacturer, &c., 63, Darwen Street, Blackburn.—This business was founded in 1854, and has enjoyed a highly successful career. The premises comprise a large shop and warehouse, heavily stocked with the various goods incidental to the trade. The works are at Hollin Bank, and here the proprietor has extensive premises that were opened in 1861. The premises are thoroughly equipped with the latest and most improved forms of patent machinery, included in which are five twisting machines, four finishing, two roping,

two balling, one banding, one warping, and one pitching machines. From end to end of the block there is a line laid for waggons and in every detail the arrangements are upon the most approved and complete style. The trade has, however, increased to such an extent that Mr. Hayes contemplates increasing his plant and machinery in order to meet the demands of his large business. The motive power for the whole of the establishment is provided by a powerful engine of the most improved construction, erected by a well-known firm in Blackburn. Mr. Hayes employs a very efficient staff, and both he and his son generally supervise all branches of the work. The trade is mostly among the leading millowners, foundries, collieries, &c., not only in the immediate locality but also generally in all parts of Blackburn, Darwen, Accrington, and north-east Lancashire, where there is an extensive and highly influential connection, which, under the proprietor's able and energetic management is still rapidly increasing.

Thomas Dugdale, Brother, & Co., Spinners and Manufacturers, Griffin Mills, Livesey, Blackburn.—This great business was founded in 1852, and its entire history has been a record of notable commercial ends accomplished and high prosperity achieved by the energetic enterprise and sound principles of its proprietors. In 1874 the senior partner, Mr. Thomas Dugdale, died, and since then the house has been under the control of the brother, Mr. Adam Dugdale, whose administration admirably illustrates the qualities of activity, experience, and judgment which mark his personal character. The firm have their headquarters at the well-known Griffin Mills, and the industry there carried on exhibits many features of splendid vitality and thorough development. The mills are two in number, and together cover an area of 13,000 square yards. Their mechanical equipment and general facilities are of the most elaborate and well-considered description, and the fine plant in operation includes 1,768 looms and 99,000 spindles, by machine makers of first-class repute. Motive power for this immense outfit of machinery is supplied by ten full-size Lancashire boilers (30 feet by 7 feet) and two hot-water boilers (100 lbs. pressure), driving four pairs of horizontal engines with an aggregate power of 2,500 horse. Upwards of twelve hundred hands are employed in these exceptionally extensive mills, and the scene of animation and activity presented by the entire establishment when in " full swing " (as it nearly always is) affords an excellent clue to the magnitude of the trade that necessitates such a vast expenditure of productive energy. Messrs. Dugdale use American cotton chiefly, though a certain quantity of Egyptian cotton is also employed in their industry. The spindle products of the Griffin Mills embrace a very large output of " Medium Counts," in yarns ; and the loom products comprise principally plain shirtings for the India and China markets. The trade controlled is one of very widespread range and extent, and the house is certainly among the most influential and typical in this important centre of the cotton industry. Mr. Adam Dugdale, J.P., the head of the firm, is an Alderman of Blackburn, and has twice held office as Mayor of the borough. Ever since he first became associated in person with the manufacturing undertakings of the town he has been highly esteemed for his active and earnest participation in all local affairs. In the discharge of his official functions he has displayed an ability akin to that put forth by him in the management of his business ; and the excellent institution of the Church of England schools at Blackburn, founded and built by the late Mr. Thomas Dugdale, and now supported entirely by Mr. Adam Dugdale, the present owner of these mills, stands as a permanent remembrancer of the deep and beneficial interest this respected gentleman has always taken in the improvement of educational resources and facilities throughout his neighbourhood.

Dutton & Co., Salford Brewery, Blackburn.—This well-known business was established about the close of the last century by the grandfather of the late Thomas Dutton. The late Mr. John Tattersall joined Mr. Thomas Dutton as managing partner some thirty-six years since, and under his supervision the present structure was built. After the decease of Mr. Dutton in 1871, the business was continued under the old style of Thomas Dutton & Co. by the surviving partner until his decease in 1878, when his brother, Wm. Tattersall, Esq., J.P. for the counties of Lancaster and Westmoreland, succeeded to the sole proprietorship of the business, which he carries on under the style of "Dutton & Co." The Salford Brewery consists of a series of blocks of splendid buildings, erected in brick and freestone, built on the tower principle. A large home trade is conducted by Messrs. Dutton & Co., of the Salford Brewery, in bitter and mild ales and porter. A very special amount of attention has been bestowed by the proprietor on the most valuable and important matter of machinery. All the appliances in and connected with the establishment are of the most recent, improved, and suitable description. Messrs. Dutton & Co., in addition to their brewery premises, have fine stabling facilities for about twenty horses, engaged in the work of conveying their goods to their various customers. The firm have acquired a special and extensive celebrity on account of their pale ales, which occupy a high position in public estimation. Messrs. Dutton & Co. hold a large number of "tied" houses in Blackburn. The firm is, in all its transactions, recognised as being of a thoroughly first-class character, and the business is carried through with that attentive consideration to the requirements of patrons which invariably results in most successful issues.

Ainsworth, Clayton & Jowett, Wholesale and Export Druggists and Manufacturing Pharmaceutical Chemists, King William Street, Blackburn.—This well-known and important business was founded nearly fifty years ago by Mr. William Ainsworth. Mr. Clayton joined the firm ten years since, being followed in the partnership by Mr. Jowett three years ago, the present actual partners in the business being Messrs. John William Clayton and William Hall Jowett, both pharmaceutical chemists and Fellows of the Chemical Society. The premises in the occupation of the firm at which the retail branch is conducted consist of a large double-fronted establishment fitted with all the necessary appliances for so important a concern. The situation is one of the finest in town. This is the only firm who prepare medicines and drugs for the doctors and surgeons of the town and surrounding districts. They also prepare and dispense private formulæ, and conduct toxicological examinations, and their stock comprises all the unofficial formulary preparations, in addition to an almost inexhaustible line in all which goes to make up the full list of a first-class drug and chemical business. Messrs. Ainsworth, Clayton & Jowett have also a business in Exchange Street, devoted to the manufacture of essences, extracts, and soluble oils used by mineral-water makers and manufacturing confectioners. The soluble essences are manufactured from the fruits they represent, and after being rendered perfectly soluble by the firm's own private processes, the marc is subjected

to hydraulic pressure equivalent to about three tons per square inch, so that the full strength and flavour is thoroughly exhausted from the fruits. Lemons, &c., are imported in very large quantities, and are peeled by machinery. This work is conducted in three floors of a front building measuring sixty feet by twenty feet. There are also other stores for stocking oils, essences, vegetable colours, drugs, &c., adjoining the premises, and a staff of from fourteen to sixteen hands are employed. This is not only a most valuable, but an ably conducted business, and the result of its efficient management is rendered apparent in the gratifying success and premier position which it enjoys.

In addition to the premises already described, Messrs. Ainsworth, Clayton & Jowett have just opened very large and central warehouses in Liverpool, of which the accompanying engraving is an accurate representation, situated at Concert Street and Fleet Street, having frontages of about 150 feet. A large quantity of new machinery is being put down here, consisting of hydraulic press of much larger dimensions and pressure than the one in Blackburn; a 4-horse power "Standard" vertical engine, with "Essex" vertical boiler. The hydraulic pressure is controlled by a brass compound tap, by means of which the ordinary water and pump pressure may be regulated with simplicity and ease at a glance. The fruit cylinder in contact with the material to be pressed is coated with block tin. In addition to the above machinery, the firm are also putting down steam pans, &c., and still and worm for the manufacture of their far-famed essences, such as ginger, &c., and also those preparations of the British Pharmacopœia which are directed to be made by distillation. The interior arrangements of the separate rooms would occupy too much space to describe, but we must say that there is no space lost, and economy combined with good arrangement, so as to be able to save time, labour, and consequently execute orders promptly, seems to have been predominant in arranging the separate departments. There is also a neat little laboratory for experimental purposes for the private use of the principals, a retired place. Every detail of the work has been carefully considered, and the Liverpool house promises to be a big success.

Roger Pomfret, Rope and Twine Manufacturer, &c., Northgate and Simmons Street, Blackburn.—In reviewing the leading establishments of the industrial and commercial world of Blackburn, special note must be taken of the establishment which is carried on under the proprietorship of Mr. Roger Pomfret, who as a rope, twine, and cotton banding manufacturer has gained a renown that extends throughout the United Kingdom, India, and the Colonies. The business has been in existence over a half of a century, having been founded in 1822 at the above address by the grandfather of the present owner, who came into possession of the business in 1876, and to whose energy, enterprise, and managerial ability the success that has been achieved may be justly attributed. The premises consist of a well-fitted and compactly arranged warehouse and office that is heavily stocked with a great assortment of every description of ropes, twines, cotton ropes, and goods of that character. In the rear of the shop, and with an entrance from Simmons Street there is a "rope-walk," two storeys high, and about 180 yards in length, where a large quantity of rope and twine of all kinds is manufactured. The goods produced in this part of the establishment are inclusive of all descriptions of twines made of both Italian and Russian hemp and cotton, and the firm are widely renowned for the undoubtedly fine quality of the goods manufactured. Among the leading specialities may be noticed rim and scroll-band, winder and spindle-band, tubular spindle-band, flax-spun yarn, hemp-spun yarn, block or hoist-rope, cotton driving-rope, dobby-cord, heald cord, piece-twine, stitchen-twine, pitch-lap, weight-rope, and a great variety of others of the same kind. A great speciality of the house is their cotton driving-ropes, which are the best in the market, and are largely superseding leather driving-belts. All goods are made on the most approved principle, and may be thoroughly relied upon as being of the very best quality of manufacture. A very efficient staff is employed, and the work is carried on under the immediate supervision of the proprietor, who is widely known, and maintains a very extensive and important connection not only in the adjacent district, but generally in all parts of the United Kingdom; and a very extensive shipping trade is done with India and our Colonial possessions.

A. Ingram & Co., Wholesale and Retail Hair, Flock, Spring, and Straw Mattress Manufacturers, 27, Darwen Street, Blackburn.—The "Old Original Bedding Warehouse" is well known in Blackburn and district, having been established by the late Thomas Ingram over forty years since, and carried on by him personally up to his death about four years ago. The premises in Darwen Street comprise a large and roomy shop or showroom, with a frontage of about 24 feet, and extending backwards about 30 feet, and a commodious and useful workroom above, where mattress making, upholstering, flock dressing, &c., used to be carried on, but owing to a much extended business has had to be removed to very much larger and more convenient premises in Clayton Street, where all the manufacturing, &c., is now done, the shop in Darwen Street being reserved solely for wholesale and retail sale business, where there is always a large assortment of iron and brass bedsteads in stock, with blankets, quilts, and sheets at all prices, and a very large stock of feathers of excellent quality is always on hand. All kinds of upholstery work is regularly executed by the firm. Feather beds are dressed, and flock beds are redressed and sent home the same day; all goods are delivered by the firm's own carts or vans within a reasonable distance; church cushions are also made to any size or colour, and all orders by post receive the most prompt attention. An extensive trade is done throughout the town and surrounding district principally of a wholesale character, while a very considerable passing retail business is also carried on. The whole is under the personal control and management of Mr. J. O'Bryan (son-in-law and brother-in-law to the late Mr. Thomas Ingram, and his daughter Miss A. Ingram), who displays a considerable amount of business energy and ability in the enterprising way in which he devotes himself to the development of every department of the establishment.

Walkden & Dixon, Paper Stainers, Brookhouse Fields, Blackburn.—This important concern was established in 1853. Mr. Walkden, the senior partner died in the year 1872, and since that date the business has been conducted by the surviving partner, Mr. Dixon. The works are of a most suitable description, and cover an area of one and a half acres, reaching to a height of three storeys. Messrs. Walkden & Dixon are busily engaged in staining and printing wall and other papers by hand, as also by specially adapted machinery. The goods of this firm are largely exported to various parts of the world, including America, India, and Australia. The premises are fitted with boiler and engine of 30-horse power, and the work of the firm engages a staff of eighty hands. Messrs. Walkden & Dixon are the only firm who have ever been engaged in a business of this class in Blackburn, and stand alone at the present date. The special feature of their work consists in the production of wall papers, a class of business in which their name is invested with a decided prominence. This important art furnishes a fine field for the exercise of artistic taste and precision in judgment, and in the goods of this firm there is an unmistakable manifestation of the qualifications which have made it so thoroughly successful, not only in Blackburn, but throughout a very large and valuable business connection.

Thomas Lewis, Carriage Builder, 1, St. Peter Street, Blackburn.—One of the oldest and most thoroughly representative firms belonging to the industry of carriage building in this district of Lancashire is that of Thomas Lewis, whose well-known carriage works are situated at 1, St. Peter Street and Mincing Lane. This business was established in the year 1868 by Mr. Lewis, the present proprietor, who in 1875 assumed his brother-in-law, Mr. John Lewis, as a partner. From this date the title of the firm was that of T. and J. Lewis until 1885, when the co-partnership was dissolved, and since then the business has been solely the property of the founder. The works of the firm which are owned by Mr. Thomas Lewis occupy a large area of ground, and comprise a handsome showroom, body-making room, trimming-room, paint-room, and large smithy, his latest addition being steam power, and machinery on the most approved principle. With a spacious yard, outhouses, and the buildings having been recently enlarged to meet the increasing demands

the establishment is admirably suited to the trade. Every description of vehicle is turned out of these works, including broughams, landaus, waggonettes, phaetons, dogcarts, &c., &c.; and the house has long enjoyed, and continues to maintain and extend, a high reputation for the excellence of the workmanship in every department. Besides being constantly busy in making new carriages to order, Mr. Lewis does a large trade in repairs, and employs a very large staff of men in this department. The trade of the firm is very extensive, and the business connection, which is of the highest class, reaches all over Lancashire and Cheshire, a large business being done with farmers, contractors, and gentry, in and around Blackburn. Mr. Lewis is a frank, courteous gentleman, well known in town, and is much respected by all who have the pleasure of meeting him, whether in connection with business or matters of public interest. Mr. Lewis was recently successful in a competition (13) for plans for a new police van for conveyance of prisoners to the Preston Gaol; and has been awarded by the Blackburn Agricultural Society: First Prize, Silver Medal, 1873; Silver Cup, 1874; Silver Cup, 1875; Silver Cup, 1876; Silver Medal, Manchester and Liverpool Show, 1881.

Wm. Sharples & Co., China Clay Importers and Merchants, 19, Water Street (Salford Bridge), Blackburn.—This business was established in 1878, and is one of a very special and important class, as china clay is used very extensively in the manufacturing and bleaching of cotton calicoes, and in paper-making. The premises at Water Street comprise an office, and also rooms used for the storage of returned empties. Messrs. William Sharples & Co. always have large stocks in bags stored at all the principal stations in their district, and large stocks in bulk at Runcorn Docks, near Liverpool. The firm purchase all their china clay in Cornwall—that unequalled centre for this mineral. The firm are represented at the Royal Exchange, Manchester (No. 5 Pillar) on Tuesdays and Fridays; and, in addition to a wide business circle throughout England, possess an extensive connection on the Continent. The importation of china clay is a work of a somewhat exclusive kind, and its transit forms a very valuable item in the statistics of British commercial enterprise. In the hands of Messrs. William Sharples & Co., of Blackburn, this business is treated and carried out with a true mercantile spirit; and so close has been the attention bestowed by the firm, and so high have they reached in the estimation of all their business friends, that their concerns in trade are at the present date most satisfactorily and persistently represented over a very wide area.

Joseph Cheshire, Woollen Merchant, 31, Church Street, Blackburn.—This business was founded by Mr. William Longfield in 1851, in premises the site of which are now occupied by Messrs. Cunliffes and Brooks' Bank. An excellent trade was soon established, and a large business was being done up to Mr. Longfield's retirement in 1866, when Mr. Cheshire took over the concern. In 1867, the business was removed to the present address, where, for over twenty years, Mr. Cheshire has carried on a large and prosperous wholesale trade. The premises comprise a large double shop, with two extensive plate-glass windows, and a frontage of about 45 feet. The large interior is exceedingly well arranged and fitted for business. The windows are tastefully set out with an excellent display of cloth pieces, in all the latest and most fashionable designs and material, giving the front of the establishment a most effective and complete appearance. The stock is exceedingly large and varied, consisting of all descriptions of Meltons, West of Englands, serges, diagonals, cheviots and other Scotch tweed, as well as all kinds of linings, calicoes, woollens, buttons, threads, braids, trimmings, &c., &c., used in the tailoring trade. The business is a very extensive one, and the trading connection extremely widespread. Experienced assistants are employed, while representatives are always " on the road," and cover a very wide area, and the firm is extremely well known, and highly respected throughout the country. Mr. Cheshire is highly respected in business circles in the town and district, and is held in the highest repute for his commercial enterprise, energy, and ability.

W. Brooks & Co., Tailors and Habit Makers, 7, New Market Street, Blackburn.—This flourishing business was established near the premises now occupied over half a century ago, the present address being the *locale* of the house for the past twenty-five years. The appointments of the establishment throughout are unique, and the street frontage most attractive. The workrooms are on the first floor, and there are employed regularly a full staff. The custom accorded the house is entirely confined to bespoke work, and for this purpose a large and comprehensive stock of cloths, such as suitings, tweeds, Meltons, Angolas, Cheviots, Cashmeres, homespuns, serges, flannels, West of England coatings, &c., is always kept on hand. The great speciality of the establishment is the making of ladies' riding habits, for which the firm have a reputation far and wide. The most prominent trade feature, however, that has formed the basis of the celebrity of the house with the public generally is the superior workmanship, which, on close investigation, will prove that the merits of the various fabrics and garments displayed, and their general finish, are all that could be desired in this branch of scientific industry. The patronage of the establishment is extensive and well-established among the better class of customers. The firm members are gentlemen of great enterprise and business ability, and held in esteem by all with whom they have commercial transactions.

Wm. Hy. Hornby & Co., Brookhouse Mills, Blackburn.—This popular and highly respected firm was founded upwards of a century ago; and although its immediate origin cannot be definitely traced, it has been in the possession of the family ever since. Mr. W. H. Hornby, now the sole member of the firm, was elected member of Parliament for Blackburn at last election. Of late years various important improvements have from time to time been effected; and notably was this the case, commencing about 1869, when a new weaving shed was added, with machinery of the most modern and improved character, since when the alterations have been almost continuous. These works at the present date occupy the enviable position of being considered one of the best combinations of weaving and spinning mills in England. The mill, in conjunction with the yard and lodge, occupies an area of fully three acres, employing a working staff of about eight hundred hands. It is finely fitted with roving and slubbing frames, carding engines, mules, &c., and represents a total of seventy-five thousand spindles. There are also twelve hundred and seventy-six looms, with engines and boilers capable of driving a thousand horse-power. The class of goods manufactured here are principally shirtings for export trade. The Brookhouse Mills are almost entirely built of stone and furnished with fire-escapes from the top to the bottom storeys. Not only is the firm of Messrs. Wm. Hy. Hornby & Co. one of the oldest and most esteemed in Lancashire, but between them and their employés there exists that feeling of good-will and kindly courtesy which requires no explanation but carries its own certificate.

William Meadowcroft & Son, Manufacturing Chemists, and Manufacturers of Essences, &c., Old Bank Street and King Street, Blackburn.—The firm of William Meadowcroft & Son was established in 1870 as mineral water manufacturers, and soon secured an excellent business. In the year 1876 they introduced the important feature of the manufacture of all kinds of essences, for which the firm has during the past thirteen years, become so celebrated. In the year 1882 the mineral water business was sold, and the firm then entirely devoted itself to the manufacturing of fruit essences, &c. The large premises in Old Bank Street soon became too little, and have been altered and added to several times since the year 1876, the last being the addition of the King Street premises, and they include now the several depart-

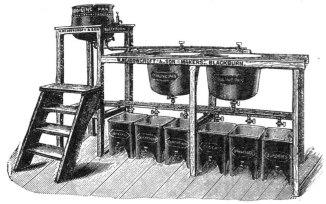

ments for manufacturing, storing, bottling, and packing in the completest manner. The manufacturing plant is especially first rate, the principal portion of it being their own invention. In one room there is a hydraulic press capable of exerting a pressure of 400 tons. This press is used for extracting the essences from lemons, oranges, &c., and is worked by a powerful gas-engine. Messrs. Meadowcroft & Son are also makers of syrup-making plants and bottle-washing machines, for the use of mineral water makers. The Model syrup plant, the invention and property of the firm, is especially ingenious and successful, and is now largely supplied by them to the trade at reasonable prices. There is a special arrangement of boiling, cooling, and mixing-pans, pipes, and taps, which is exceedingly simple and satisfactory, and by it syrups are made quickly, easily, and with perfect cleanliness. The syrup comes only in contact with enamel and block tin. The special advantages claimed for

this plant are—its great strength, durability, and compactness, the ease with which all taps, &c., can be removed; the contact being only with enamel and pure block tin; there is no waiting for cold syrup, as the cooling-pans are arranged to work alternately; and finally, no carrying whatever of the syrup is necessary, as the whole of the mixing-pans can be supplied with plain cold syrup from either of the cooling-pans. The bottle-washing machines, when worked by four lads, are capable of turning out one thousand dozens of ginger beer bottles, washed, brushed, and rinsed out with cold water, per day of ten hours. Among the many manufactured products, for which the firm is now so well and favourably known, may be named all kinds of soluble fruit essences, including lemon, orange (bitter), orange (sweet), Jamaica ginger, ginger ale, jargonelle pear, pineapple, ginger champagne, hop ale, dandelion stout, raspberry, strawberry, black currant, limes, vanilla, Tonquin, champagne, fizz, aniseed, &c. They also import largely essential oils, pure,

and of the very finest quality, of lemon, orange (bitter and sweet), peppermint, clove, aniseed, almond, lime, cassia, wintergreen, geranium, neroli, and otto de rose. They also manufacture foamine, for producing a rich creamy head of foam on aërated waters, beers, &c., also burnt sugar colouring for the mineral water trade; acids of various kinds, citric, tartaric, and salicylic, &c., and hop ale essence of double the usual strength. Messrs. Meadowcroft & Son specially call attention to their concentrated soluble essence of lemon, which is prepared from the finest Messina lemons by an entirely new process. This essence is by far the strongest, and therefore the cheapest in the market, and imparts the true flavour and aroma of the fresh fruit. There is also their concentrated soluble essence of orange, of Jamaica ginger, and of ginger ale. This latter essence is three times the usual strength, and is acknowledged to be the very best for the purpose of flavouring ginger ale, &c. It imparts the flavour and aroma of the finest ginger, in combination with lemon, vanilla, rose, &c., and produces a beverage, with full rich body, and equal in every respect to the well-known Belfast ginger ale. Messrs. Meadowcroft's trade is entirely wholesale, extending principally over the northern and midland counties of England. They also do a certain amount of export business with India and Australia. Several travellers are constantly "on the road," so that the firm and its products are well known over a very extensive area. A considerable number of hands are regularly employed on the premises, and large though the output is, it is barely sufficient to meet the demands upon its resources. The frequent additions that have of late years been made to the original premises have exhausted all possible chances of further increase, and the purchase of a new site and the erection of entirely new works has been decided upon. The new works are in course of erection, and will be about double the size of the present ones. The new address will be Regent Street.

John F. Polding, Corn Merchant, Darwen Street and Salford Bridge, Blackburn.—This business was founded as far back as the year 1802 by Mr. John Polding, who retired in 1847, being succeeded by Mr. John Polding and Mr. Henry Polding, sons of the above gentleman, and subsequently came into the hands of the present proprietor, Mr. John F. Polding, in 1884. The firm's establishment in Darwen Street forms the headquarters, and is situated in an old-fashioned building which was erected two hundred years ago and has walls eight feet in thickness, oak beams and rafters. But although old there are few more substantial and handsomely fitted places of business in the country, the present proprietor having made extensive internal improvements. With eight spacious rooms and a large counting-house, it is admirably suited for the trade of the corn dealer, and, like the more extensive premises at Salford Bridge, is stocked with corn flour, beans, peas, and every kind of cereals. The premises at Salford Bridge comprise a handsome shop, which occupies a building of three storeys in height and a warehouse of four storeys, both of which contain valuable stocks of the goods dealt in by the firm and have telephonic communication with the headquarters and the Exchange. Besides these, Mr. Polding has a branch at Fleet Street, Preston. The trade is very extensive, and the business connection, which reaches all over Lancashire, is as old and substantial as the house itself, being chiefly with farmers and gentry, amongst whom a large trade is done in the districts around Blackburn. It should be mentioned that the founder of this business and his son (the present proprietor's father) played an important part in local politics, having both occupied the honourable position of alderman in Blackburn, and although Mr. Polding does not take a prominent part in public affairs he is well known in influential circles and much respected by all with whom he comes in contact for the warm interest he takes privately in all matters affecting the interests of his fellows.

Robert Hogg, Heald and Reed Maker, Moorgate Heald and Reed Works, Blackburn.—This business was established in the year 1874 by Mr. Hogg, who is now the foremost manufacturer of healds and reeds in this district of Lancashire. Moorgate Heald and Reed Works cover a large area of ground, and consist of a building of three storeys in height, with out-houses. They are equipped in first-class style with all the most approved modern machinery, including reed-making, doubling, knitting, and varnishing machines by the foremost makers, and having been extended and re-arranged from time to time, as the demand for the firm's products increased, they are admirably suited for the extensive business carried on. The upper floor is known as the winding flat, where the yarns are wound on bobbins preparatory to being doubled, which operation is performed by doubling machinery having 1,200 spindles. After doubling, the yarn is taken to the second floor, where the knitting and varnishing machines are situated, and made into healds, of which the machines turn out 1,600 sets per week. The reed-making is carried on in the ground flat, where the machines for that purpose are situated, as well as those for doubling. The machinery is driven by a steam-engine of 25-horse power, by Ashton & Frost, Limited, and the boiler, which is of the Lancashire type, and 30 feet long by 7 feet in diameter, is one of Dewhurst's, of Church. The trade of the firm, in which sixty hands are employed, is the most extensive in Blackburn, and reaches all over north-east Lancashire, where the house is represented by three travellers. Mr. Hogg is a well-known gentleman, who has won the prominent position he enjoys through hard work, sparing no expense of machinery and appliances, and honourable methods in the management in his business. Telephone 104.

W. Garside's Victoria Restaurant, and Garside's Commercial and Temperance Hotel and Fielding Arms, Blackburn.

—The above establishment is one of the finest of its kind in the district, and was formerly known as the Market Coffee Tavern. It was subsequently taken over by Mr. W. Garside, who has since conducted it with a very commendable spirit of enterprise. The premises are of considerable extent, and comprise a spacious building of four storeys, having an imposing frontage. The whole of the establishment has been fitted in first-class style, the chief object being to ensure the comfort and convenience of the numerous visitors by whom the establishment is patronised. It has a very superior appearance, and is admirably arranged in every detail. On the first and second floors there are splendid dining-rooms, capable of accommodating between two hundred and three hundred persons, and all the other arrangements are upon a similarly liberal scale. There are a large grill-room, dining, smoking, and billiard-rooms (the latter being supplied with three tables), and all other necessary apartments. The kitchens are in the basement, and are fitted upon the most approved methods, both in their relation to sanitary arrangements and in all other considerations. The establishment is probably most renowned for grilled chops and steaks, and Mr. Garside is the only proprietor in the town who supplies them in this form. The speciality dinner of three courses may be fairly regarded as a marvel, and how the proprietor manages to do it at the price is a thing which, as a certain well-known nobleman once or twice remarked, "no fellah can understand." Mr. Garside is, however, essentially enterprising, and he undoubtedly does the largest business in Blackburn, and has a reputation second to none. A point that requires special notice is that everything is so scrupulously clean, and done in superior style. Mr. Garside conducts his business on the very best lines, and notwithstanding the remarkably moderate scale of charges everything is served "decently and in order." A speciality of the house is the catering for all descriptions of school, wedding, pic-nic, and ball parties, and cutlery and all requisites for the above let out on hire. In addition to the above the proprietor has two more extensive establishments, one at 29 and 31, King Street, termed the Commercial and Temperance Hotel, fitted up with a first-class suite of bedrooms, twenty-four in number, and all other conveniences, not to be surpassed in the district; and another, occupying a commanding site at the junction of Darwen Street and Back Lane, known as the "Fielden Arms," fitted up with large and commodious rooms for dancing, pic-nic, and presentation parties. Large dining and smoke rooms, and one of the cheapest dinners in the town, will here be found. Mr. Garside thus commands a very large trade, and is widely renowned in all directions.

Thomas Leigh, Medical Botanist, 69, King Street,

corner of Byrom Street, opposite the "Wellington Inn," Blackburn.—Prominent among the medical establishments of the town appears the centrally-situated depôt of the celebrated medical botanist, Mr. Thomas Leigh, the sole proprietor, the business having been established in 1853. Mr. Leigh is the owner of this valuable property, and from time to time various alterations have been made in harmony with the development of the business, so that attractive frontages now abut on both Byrom and King Streets. The spacious windows are set out with the usual insignia of coloured bottles, and the general display vouchsafed to chemists, though the practice here carried on is confined to medical botany. The rooms over the shop are used exclusively for the storage of herbs, English and foreign, and other dry goods used in the botanic practice. The proprietor has had over twenty years' practical experience and unrivalled success in treating all kinds of diseases, and is convinced of the vital importance of using only organic medicines, and confidently asserts that all persons placing themselves under his treatment will have the advantage of a permanent cure, in a short time, which for simplicity and safety cannot be equalled. Numerous specialities are prepared by Mr. Leigh, notably his celebrated cough mixture, which gives instant relief and ultimately effects a permanent cure in the most irritating cough. Sufferers should try it. His tic or neuralgia mixture is likewise an unrivalled preparation for successfully grappling with the troublesome malady for which it is prescribed. While supplying everything required in the botanical science of medicine, the social element is not overlooked, for here can also be obtained the famous "Tower Tea," imported by the Great Tower Street Tea Company, of London, which is a tea of sound, even leaf, and very strong and full flavoured in the cup, with fine quality, and offered at two shillings a-pound. All lovers of a delicious cup of tea should try it without delay. Herbs, barks, roots, flowers, seeds, &c., are supplied at this mart wholesale and retail, though the bulk of the trade is of the latter class, and well established throughout Blackburn and the surrounding districts.

Walmsley & Charnley, Wine and Spirit Importers,

12, Station Road, Blackburn.—This business has been in existence just over a quarter of a century, and has throughout enjoyed a highly successful career. The sole partner is now Mr. John Charnley, to whose individual ability and energy much of the success achieved may be very justly attributed. The premises consist of a large building of three floors, and having an imposing frontage of about fifty feet and ample cellarage accommodation. On the ground floor are the offices, &c., adjoining these being the goods entrance; while in the rear are the store and various rooms devoted to different operations and processes in the trade. The floors above are also used as stores, and the whole of the establishment, including the cellars, is heavily stocked with a very choice assortment of high-class wines and spirits in every variety. The firm are very large importers, some of the vintages on hand being of great age, and therefore especially valuable. The trade covers a wide scope of operations, all descriptions of wines being dealt in so long as they are of the requisite high standard of quality. A large business is also done in spirits, in which the stock is extensive and valuable, and includes all the most renowned makes that have become so popular, especially their special blend of old Highland and Glenlivet whiskey. The firm do a large trade, and are widely known.

F. Turner, Coach Builder, &c., Eagle Carriage Works,

Starkie Street, Blackburn.—Mr. Turner commenced business in 1879, at premises in Clayton Street. He removed to Tontine Street in 1880, and finally to his present roomy and commodious premises in Starkie Street in 1885. These comprise a large four-storey building and extensive yard, covering altogether about an acre of ground, and affording every facility for carrying on a large business in all its details. The ground floor of the building is a large workshop, exceedingly well arranged and fitted up with forges and bellows worked by steam-power, as well as circular and band saws, boring machines, &c., &c. Here also is a powerful nine-horse steam engine and boiler, which supplies all the necessary power used throughout the establishment. The next floor is fitted with stands for carriages, which are built here; the whole of the painting and varnishing of the establishment, carriages of all kinds, carts, lurries, &c., is done here in the best style of workmanship. A large and valuable stock is always to be seen in this department. The second floor is entirely used as a storeroom for conveyances of various kinds and for warehousing timber for use in the workshops below; while the top floor is devoted to the drying and careful seasoning of the wood. A large and valuable stock of timber, both new and seasoned, is always on hand. About a dozen able and experienced men are regularly employed in the various departments of the business, and a considerably widespread trade is done both in new work and in repairs. All jobbing work is punctually attended to; old carriages, &c., are taken by the firm in part exchange for new ones. The whole of the concern is carried on under the special control and supervision of the proprietor himself, who is now well known both in the town and surrounding district, so patrons and customers can depend upon their orders and commissions being executed with the greatest skill, care, and promptitude.

J. S. Duxbury, Paper Merchant, Printer, and Paper Bag Manufacturer, Cleaver Street Mill, Blackburn.

—This business, which is the foremost of its kind in this district, was established in the year 1877 by Mr. Duxbury and is still carried on under that name. The establishment is of large extent, occupying a building of three storeys, and consists of paper warehouse, with printing works and office on the ground floor, paper bag manufactory on the floor above, and store-rooms on the upper flat. Equipped with all the most approved modern machinery and appliances, which are driven by steam power, and employing a large staff of operatives, these works turn out an immense quantity of goods, including printed parcelling paper and every quality and size of printed paper bags for grocers, confectioners, tea dealers, drapers, milliners and other trades. The firm's business connection is very extensive and reaches all over Lancashire, a large business being done in and around Blackburn. Hard work, a thoroughly practical knowledge of the business in all its details, and honourable methods in the management are among the secrets by which Mr. Duxbury has won the prominent position the firm now enjoys in this important trade. But doubtless the reputed artistic taste, the promptitude that has always been observed in the execution of urgent orders, have helped to secure the high place now held in the esteem and confidence of a numerous connection.

Lupton & Jackson's General Drapers, &c., Establishment, 33 and 35, Higher Eanam, Blackburn.

—This business, which is one of the foremost of its kind in Blackburn, was established in 1887 by the present sole proprietors, who are located in a handsome warehouse with large showroom in the rear. Lighted by large plate-glass windows, which are most tastefully arranged, the warehouse displays a splendid stock of high-class drapery goods. These comprise dress stuffs in all the most fashionable shades, jackets and mantles in every style, showing artistic taste and practical skill in the designs and workmanship. Ties, collars, cuffs, shawls, laces, gloves, trimmings, and every description of drapery and hosiery goods are also in great variety, as well as carpets, bedsteads, and bedding. The trade is very extensive, and is rapidly increasing, this being due in a great measure to the excellent quality of the materials dealt in. The firm's mantles are made in the most fashionable style, and exceedingly moderate prices are charged in every department. The members of this popular firm are agreeable, courteous gentlemen, and their efforts to bring the highest class of goods within the reach of all classes have won for them a high place in the esteem and confidence of their numerous warm supporters, who, by recommending the house to their friends, are saving Messrs. Lupton & Jackson the expense of a traveller

J. Baldwin (Executors of), Ironmongers, Church Street, Blackburn.—The business carried on under the above title is probably one of the oldest of its kind in Lancashire, having been founded over one hundred years ago by a Mr. Butcher, who was succeeded by Mr. Smith; finally, it came into the hands of the late Mr. John Baldwin, and since his decease has been carried on by the executors. The premises comprise a large corner block, having a frontage to Church Street of upwards of forty feet and a depth of over one hundred and fifty feet. The principal shop is stocked with a choice assortment of goods of a miscellaneous and varied character. The upper floors are used as showrooms and warehouses, and are throughout stocked with an enormous supply of goods. In the rear the building is entirely devoted to storage and the premises are fitted with a powerful hoist. The whole of the establishment is kept in excellent order, and the showrooms, which are arranged with commendable regard to effect, present a highly elegant and attrac-

tive appearance. Chief among the items of the stock may be noticed such as marble mantelpieces, dining and drawing-room grates, ranges, gasaliers, lamps, hall lamps, household irons and brasses, shop and other fittings in brass and iron, and a large assortment of ironmongery incidental to general furnishing purposes. The leading speciality is a heating apparatus for churches, halls, conservatories, &c., at high and low pressure, a modern invention that has been introduced to the public with very great success. The firm do a large amount of work in what may be termed the practical department of industries connected with metals, and execute all kinds of contracts in the work of whitesmiths and bellhangers. They also undertake to furnish mills with various descriptions of machinery and appliances, and are therefore well known among the leading manufacturers. In every branch of the business it is conducted upon high-class lines, and there are few houses that have such an undeniably excellent reputation. A large staff is employed, and a very extensive trade is done. A branch establishment was opened at Clitheroe four years ago, and has met with much success.

Thompson Bros., Tailors and Juvenile Costumiers, 50, Market Place, Blackburn.—This business was established in 1881 by the present proprietors, and an excellent trade was soon secured, which is still on the increase. The premises comprise a large four-storey building, the ground floor forming a large single shop, with a frontage of twenty-six feet, and one large plate-glass window. The shop is extremely lofty, and extends backwards about forty-five feet. Above the shop there are four large store-rooms, and two well-arranged, roomy, and extensive workshops, where about twenty handy and experienced men are employed, and where most of the goods sold on the premises are made. The large shop is exceedingly well arranged, while the fittings are all in excellent taste. The extensive window is most elaborately dressed, and presents a most attractive appearance to the passer by; while the interior is well filled with triumphs of the costumier's art, in all the latest styles and cuts, and for all ages and conditions. In addition to the enormous supply of ready-made goods, there is also always on hand an extremely large stock of woollen cloths, tweeds, Meltons, &c., of the most popular and fashionable patterns and designs, according to the season; as well as linings and all other goods used in the tailoring trade. Besides their large ready-made trade, Messrs. Thompson Bros. do an excellent middle-class bespoke business in which they are enabled to give the greatest satisfaction to their large *clientèle*, in the essential matters of cut, material, fit, and price, so that no surprise need be expressed at the rapid and still increasing growth of their large business. The whole of the departments of the establishment are under the personal management and direct superintendence of the proprietors themselves, who have spared neither time, labour, capital, nor enterprise in bringing the concern up to its present stage of comparative perfection.

Mrs. E. Houlker, Wholesale and Retail Draper, Milliner, Dress and Mantle Maker, 9, Sudell Cross, Blackburn.—There are comparatively few concerns in the drapery, &c., line, which have had a successful run of a quarter of a century without a break in the proprietorship, or in the introduction of what is termed "new blood" in the character of a partner or partners. The emporium under notice, however, of which Mrs. E. Houlker is the sole principal, was opened by this lady in the year 1864, at the present address, 9, Sudell Cross, and a more thoroughly representative house in the same branch of business is not to be found in Blackburn. Mrs. Houlker has had a most successful career, and, at this time, her establishment is one of the best known and most extensively patronised in the town. The premises are both spacious and handsome, and are conveniently situate. They comprise a double shop having an area of about 30 by 18 feet, beautifully fitted up and appointed, and furnished with large plate-glass windows, well designed for the display of goods. Both externally and internally the appearance is highly attractive. In addition, there is a fine, well ventilated workroom, which is capable of accommodating a considerable staff of assistants engaged in the millinery, dress-making, and mantle-making departments. The stock is in every branch first class, and all the garments offered for sale are made up on the premises. The goods are not only of the best materials and workmanship, but in the very newest styles of fashion, and, as regards costumes, &c., a perfect fit is guaranteed, and orders of every description are executed with the utmost promptitude. A speciality of the house is the supply of mourning costumes, &c., and in this department it has acquired a most superior repute. Mourning and also wedding orders are undertaken on very reasonable terms, and the greatest possible care is bestowed upon their execution. Mrs. Houlker has always Madam Demorest's paper patterns in stock, and we may add that she is the agent for the celebrated dyers and cleaners, P. & P. Campbell, of Perth. Referring once more to the stock, we may state that it comprises drapery of every description, millinery, dresses, &c., also a choice collection of furs in great variety, and all the wares are, taking quality into account, remarkably cheap. Mrs. Houlker possesses a most valuable connection in Blackburn and the neighbourhood, and, personally, is exceedingly popular and widely respected.

Peter Pickering, Brush Manufacturer, Church Street, Blackburn (Telephone 165).—Founded in the year 1825 by Mr. Peter Pickering, this business since his death, which occurred in 1850, has been conducted by his trustees, by whose efforts the old-established reputation of the firm has continued to be maintained. The premises consist of a handsome double shop with a large building in the rear of three storeys in height, which is occupied as warehouses and works. On the ground floor of this building are three large rooms, one of them being devoted to storage purposes, the second and third floors being used as workrooms. A large staff of hands is employed in producing brushes of every description for public works and domestic purposes. The warehouse is most tastefully arranged, and displays a splendid stock of the firm's manufactures, as well as all other cleansing requisites, such as washleathers, scouring flannel, furniture polish, emery cloth and powder. There is also a valuable stock of cocoa matting, mats, and skins, in various colours and sizes. The trade of the house is very extensive, and the business connection, which is of the most influential order, reaches all over Blackburn and into the surrounding districts for many miles, a large business being done with mills and shopkeepers, farmers and gentry, the latter being large buyers of the firm's brushes for use in stables, and for which class of brushes the house has enjoyed a high reputation for more than half a century. The manager of this important business, Mr. Pickering, is an agreeable, courteous gentleman, and enjoys a high place in the esteem and confidence of the firm's numerous warm supporters for the promptitude observed in executing urgent orders and the honourable methods that characterise his management.

William A. Metcalfe, Watchmaker, Jeweller, &c., 18, King William Street, Blackburn.—Mr. Metcalfe commenced business here in 1878, and has established an excellent connection. The premises comprise an attractive double shop, with plate-glass windows, in which the display of watches, plated goods, and jewellery is exceedingly rich. The interior arrangements and fittings are of the most complete and tasteful character. The stock is a most heavy and valuable one, embracing gold and silver watches, and clocks of all kinds, gold and silver jewellery in the latest styles and designs, bracelets, brooches, earrings, necklets, studs, &c., &c.; wedding rings and dress rings in great variety and of considerable value; gold and silver chains; as well as plated goods of all kinds. There is also an excellent assortment of silver and electro-plated articles in all the most fashionable designs; as well as barometers, thermometers, aneroids, &c., &c., making altogether a most elegant and valuable lot of stock, the whole of which is arranged in the best taste and to the best advantage. The whole interior, indeed, would not suffer materially when put in competition with some of the best Manchester and metropolitan establishments. Repairs, &c, are carefully attended to on the premises, under the personal supervision of Mr. Metcalfe himself, who is a thoroughly practical watchmaker, and has had long experience in the trade. Able assistants are employed, but the whole establishment is under the management of the proprietor himself.

James Gregson, Gun Maker, Wholesale and Retail Fishing-Rod and Tackle Manufacturer, Penny Street, Blackburn.—This business, which is the foremost, and, as a manufacturing concern, the only one in Blackburn, was established in the present premises in 1873 by Mr. Gregson, who is still the sole proprietor. The premises are of large extent, comprising a fine front shop, with spacious warehouse above and large works in the rear. The works are equipped in first-class style, with all the most approved machinery and some special appliances for the manufacture and repairing of sporting guns, and everything required by the angler and other sportsmen, including an important speciality for anglers invented by Mr. Gregson, who personally is a keen sportsman. The speciality referred to is that of a most ingenious application to fishing-rods of every kind whereby the joints are made secure against "flying out" as if they were in one solid piece, and at the same time keeping the rings in a straight line from end to end. This clever arrangement (which is patented) consists of a flat spring fixed to the outside of the ferrules and having a pin fixed to the loose end which goes through a small hole in the ferrule and into one in the part of the rod which fits into the ferrule. A rod having this simple spring-clasp joint is

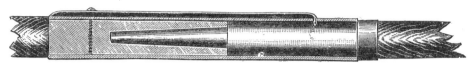

put together in the shortest possible time, and is at once ready for use without fear of derangement, as the separate pieces can neither turn in their sockets nor come out of them with the roughest usage. Being of nickel silver, these new patent spring-clasp joints do not corrode, and form an artistic ornament to a rod. The cost of mounting them upon trout rods up to 12 feet is 1s. per joint, and upon salmon rods 2s. 6d. per joint, the clasps being extra strong for these. Amongst the other classes of goods manufactured by this firm space will permit of only a few being mentioned, such as fishing hooks, landing nets of every description, brass reels, check reels, bronzed revolving plate handles, superior revolving plate reels for salmon and other kinds; silk plaited lines, spun hair reel lines, London patent fly lines; patented plaited silk and hair fly lines, gut casting lines, flies, gut in hanks, drawn gut, stone fly, and every description of hooks, floats, &c., &c. The firm's warehouse above the front shop contains an immense stock of grouse cartridges, D. Anson and Deeley's double-barrelled breechloading guns, the dimensions of which are 28 inches in barrel, twelves bore, and 6½ lbs. in weight, as well as a valuable stock of explosives, including Shultz, E.C., Curtis & Harvey, and Messrs. Eley's, Kynock & Co.'s powders, sporting cartridges, &c., of all descriptions. Tastefully fitted up and arranged the front warehouse exhibits a splendid stock of the firm's manufactures,

GREGSON'S PATENT BLACKBURN.

besides an immense assortment of all the most approved modern requisites for sportsmen, including baskets, pannier straps, wading stockings and trousers, gaiters or brogues, fishing-rods of every size and for every purpose, guns, and everything that a sportsman could ask for belonging to implements. The trade of the firm is very extensive and the business connection, which is both wholesale and retail, extends all over the United Kingdom and is of the most influential order, an extensive business being done in both departments with the foremost merchants and leading gentlemen in the country, especially in the Anson and Deeley hammerless guns and grouse cartridges, of which he makes a speciality, and for which he has received testimonials from a great many of the leading sportsmen of the district; and the patent spring-clasp joints, the latter having received the highest praise in the press and brought upwards of one thousand unsolicited testimonials from the highest authorities on the gentle craft from all quarters. Among the secrets of this firm's success are Mr. Gregson's long experience as an enthusiastic angler, his powers of invention, and his twenty years' experience as a practical maker of sportsmen's requisites. But doubtless the moderate prices charged for his unsurpassed manufactures in every department, enabling him to demand *cash* for his goods in every transaction, and the honourable methods that have always characterised the management of his business, have helped him to gain the prominent and well-deserved position he enjoys as one of the foremost makers of sportsmen's requisites in the kingdom.

S. Seed & Son, Black and Whitesmiths, Machinists, Makers of Bicycles and Tricycles, and General Ironmongers, Darwen Street Iron Works, Blackburn.—This business was founded at 4 and 5, High Street, Salford, Blackburn, by Mr. Samuel Seed in 1854. In 1885 Mr. Seed died, and since then the business has been carried on by his son, Mr. William James Seed, who removed to the present more commodious premises shortly after his father's death. The works are of large extent, and are equipped in first-rate style with smithy and all the most

approved tools, including lathes, verticals, &c., required for the manufacture of drilling machines, punching presses, loom cranks and fittings, bicycles and tricycles, pipe wrenches, and executing repairs of every description belonging to the trade of the blacksmith, whitesmith, machinist, and millwright. In front of the works there is a show-room where a splendid selection of the firm's products is exhibited, including Seed's improved drilling machines for hand and power, and having rising and falling tables; Seed's pipe wrench, a very cleverly designed tool used by plumbers, gasfitters, &c., and a display of handsome bicycles and tricycles, with everything in the shape of furnishings for these vehicles. Some of these bicycles and tricycles are of the firm's own manufacture, but a large number are by Humber & Co., Limited; Quadrant Tricycle Company, and Singer's cycles, including their new rapids; Rover's, and Star bicycles and tricycles. For these firms Mr. Seed is the sole agent here, and in the sale and repairing of them, enamelling, burnishing, and plating, letting bicycles and tricycles on hire, and in the manufacture of the "Seed" safety bicycles and tricycles the firm does a very extensive trade, which reaches fifty miles round Blackburn, and requires the services of a large staff of highly skilled tradesmen. A speciality of the house, designed for the present season, is the Seed Ladies' Safety, which is either adapted for lady or gentleman, having a detachable staff, an improvement used by no other maker. Mr. Seed has had a long practical training in every department of the mechanical arts, and is specially skilled in the manufacture of bicycles and tricycles, this being recognised by the Cyclists' Touring Club, which appointed him to execute all repairs on the vehicles belonging to its members. Possessing a frank, courteous manner, and conducting his business on straightforward principles, Mr. Seed is much liked by his numerous warm supporters and all with whom he comes in contact.

Thomas Craven, Bold Street Saw Mills, Planing and Moulding Mills, Blackburn.—This business was founded by the present proprietor in 1863. In 1864 premises were taken in Wall Street, removing in 1872 to the present premises, which were, in 1888, rebuilt throughout. The building as now constituted is two storeys high, with two yards of considerable extent, one being placed at the back for the purpose of storing logs, and over which there is a powerful travelling crane, the other in front being for deals, &c. There are two very extensive sheds for storing mahogany and other woods, moulds, veneers, &c., and also properly appointed offices, engine and boiler-house, and saw mills; a store being placed above the boiler for the purpose of drying timber. Above this, again, is a cistern capable of holding over 4,000 gallons of water, which is caught from the different roofs, and used for supplying the boiler with water, thus making a great saving of the town's water. Adjoining this on each side are the two mills. Here the machinery is excellent, and comprises the largest horizontal saw-frame in Lancashire, with engine in combination, circular saws, deal frame, band-saw, planing, trying up, moulding and other machines. The second storey contains the joiners' shop, where there are circular sawing, boring, mortising, tenoning, and other machines. The engine and boiler are by the well-known firm of Wm. & Jno. Yates, of Blackburn, and the machinery is mostly from Robinson & Son, of Rochdale. In addition to the premises referred to is a yard opposite the works, for the purpose of storing deals. Mr. Craven is at present completing a very large contract at Stoneyhurst College, which has been in progress since 1876. The establishment is in all its bearings a model of its kind, both as to construction and its splendid equipment of machinery; and the large and widespread trade of its proprietor is conducted with that taste, energy, and intelligence which ever characterises a thoroughly practical man.

George Corbishley, Mattress Manufacturer, 22, Whalley Banks, King Street, Blackburn.—Mr. George Corbishley is a wholesale flock and straw mattress manufacturer, with premises at No. 22, Whalley Banks, King Street, Blackburn. Mr. Corbishley only commenced business during the course of the year 1888, and has made a most promising beginning. The premises comprise an excellent and roomy shop or show-room on the ground floor, while overhead are four large and commodious rooms, devoted to the manufacturing of mattresses and upholstering work. These are not yet at full swing, though Mr. Corbishley has already made an effective start in this department as well. A large quantity of mattress making is already in progress, and before long the whole of the available space will be occupied in this work. A warehouse has been recently erected at the rear of the shop, to be devoted to the general manufacture. The front shop is already well stocked with a first-class assortment of bedsteads of all kinds, mattresses, and beds, and business has already been done to a very successful and promising extent. So far the business is all of a wholesale character, and is confined to Blackburn and the district surrounding. One representative is at present "on the road," and as the best goods in the trade are being supplied by Mr. Corbishley there is every prospect that the new firm will ere long take a respectable position in the trade of the district.

Wm. Almond, Neats-foot Oil and Tallow Manufac-turer, George Street West, Blackburn.—The extensive business carried on by Mr. W. Almond, neats-foot oil and tallow manufacturer, &c., presents many features of more than ordinary interest, and has increased so rapidly that it is now one of the largest and most representative establishments of its kind in the United Kingdom. Established in 1872 by the present pro-prietor, the business has gradually increased to its present gigantic pro-portions. The works are situated in George Street West, Blackburn, and occupy the greater part of an acre of ground, mostly covered with large two-storey buildings, in which the various operations are carried out. The different departments are fitted with special machinery and appliances; and upwards of thirty hands are regularly employed. The works at all times present a busy and animated scene of industrial activity. Mr. Almond does a very large and increasing business as a neats-foot oil and tallow manufacturer, refiner, wholesale tripe dresser, and as a dealer in ox

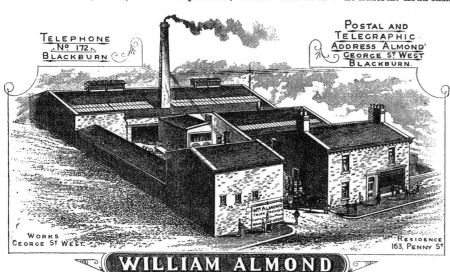

shanks, hoofs, &c. He has a widespread connection, the wholesale and retail departments operating extensively in Blackburn, where branch estab-lishments have been opened at Central Aisle, Market House; 163, Penny Street; 56, Darwen Street; 71, Lower Audley Street; and 30, Salford; as well as various establishments in other towns in different parts of Lan-cashire and Yorkshire. A great feature in this business is the guaranteed purity of the firms' neats-foot oil. They supply the principal railway com-panies in the kingdom, do an export trade through their numerous agents throughout the United Kingdom with all parts of the world; they have also a large connection amongst the steamship companies and the large spinners and manufacturers of the district, thus testifying to the magni-tude of the trade which is so successfully carried on. The business in every department receives the strict personal attention of the proprietor. The mercantile branch is conducted in a spacious suite of well-appointed offices and counting-house, having telephonic communication (No. 172), and all the accessories of a thoroughly organized establishment. The postal and telegraphic address is "Almond," George Street West, Black-burn; and the residence of the proprietor 163, Penny Street. Mr. Almond has been long and honourably connected with Blackburn, and his well-known integrity, sound judgment, and genial courtesy have secured his recognition in a wide sphere as an energetic and enterprising man, with whom it is pleasant and profitable to have business transactions.

Oliver Abbott, Milliner, Hosier, Glover, Laceman, &c., 76, King William Street, Blackburn.—Mr. Oliver Abbott commenced business only two years and a half ago, and his premises are the hand-somest and the most attractive in appearance of any in the same line of business in Blackburn. His shop is large and very commodious, having two plate-glass windows, which are most tastefully dressed. The goods are all fresh and have been carefully selected, the newest prevailing styles having been studiously kept in view, and the variety of goods as well as the price and quality have received the proprietor's most par-ticular attention. These goods comprise fancy drapery and millinery of every description—furs, gloves, hosiery, ribbons, flowers, feathers, laces, trimmings, and the many other articles of small wares that go to constitute the stock-in-trade of a first-class hosier, glover, and laceman. The nature of these goods demand a constant succession of change in styles and forms and affords unlimited scope for the display of

artistic and refined taste, which is exercised to the full in this establish-ment. In few other places of business are the goods in every detail more thoroughly representative of this high-class trade. The whole establishment is well appointed throughout, and is constantly under the proprietor's immediate supervision. Though the business was commenced so recently a large general connection has already been formed and is daily increasing. Mr. Abbott's well-known integrity has gained him the confidence of many commercial friends, and all wish the greatest success to his spirited enterprise.

Jackson & Co., Drug Stores, 9, Regent's Buildings, Larkhill, Blackburn.—The drug store is at the present day a necessity of our social arrangements. It is also under the influence of commercial con-siderations, and the druggist must also study the market prices of the goods he trades in. As an example of how they push this business, Messr. Jackson & Co.'s list of prices is an ample testimony, and the enterprising spirit with which the firm have undertaken to provide the community of Black-burn with drugs and medicines at the most moderate prices is worthy of all praise and de-serving of every encouragement. The business was established by the firm in 1885 in their pre-sent premises, which consist of a large double shop, with two plate-glass windows, having the usual accessories of a drug store of the most superior kind. The stock comprises drugs, patent medi-cines of every description, and the firm's own preparation of cod liver oil of the finest quality, which is highly recommended by the medical profession. Malt and beef wines, which are especially suited for invalids, foods for infants and invalids, including extract of meat, King's wheaten food, cooked oatmeal ready for use, Neave's, Ridge's, and Robinson's farinaceous food, and the genuine dairy-maid brand of Swiss milk. Of plasters, chest protectors, and cork soles there is an endless variety. All these goods are of splendid value at the list prices, and can defy all competition. Messrs. Jackson & Co. buying all goods direct from the makers in large quantities for cash, gives them a great advan-tage in making sale prices. Another speciality of the firm is that they retain in stock a large quantity of the best British and foreign wines which they sell at remarkably low prices. The great enterprise with which this business has been conducted continues to maintain and extend the firm's well-merited fame, working people being specially grateful for the boon of cheap medicines. The connection has become very widespread, and includes not only the general public, but many leading members of the medical profession have recommended their particular specialities.

J. E. Harrison & Co., Wholesale Tea Merchants, Mincing Lane, Blackburn.—This business which is the foremost of its kind in Blackburn was established by Mr. Harrison in the year 1875, under the present title. The establishment is of large extent, occupying a building of three storeys in height with extensive cellars. It is admi-rably fitted up and arranged for the extensive trade carried on and con-sists of a handsome sales warehouse and office on the ground floor with storage and packing rooms on those above. The stock consists entirely of teas and coffee and is a very large one. With assistants, representa-tives outside and a business connection extending throughout the northern counties, this firm does a very extensive trade; and the honour-able methods, experience and energy through which the business was formed continues to maintain and extend the old-established reputation of the house. Mr. Harrison is a well-known gentleman who is much respected by all with whom he meets whether in connection with business or matters affecting the public interests.

John Smith Baron (late Miles Baron & Son), **Tailor, Stay and Corset Maker**, Astley Gate and Corporation Street, Blackburn.—This flourishing business was founded by Mr. Miles Baron, who was one of the commissioners and afterwards a town councillor and alderman for the borough, and was subsequently carried on under the title of "Miles Baron & Son," and so continued until 1867, when the present designation was adopted. The establishment is divided into two departments, viz., tailoring and stay-making, both of which are well stocked. The latter branch, however, constitutes the speciality for which the house has a high reputation throughout the town, and the specimens of stays and corsets to be seen in grand display in every material and style known to the trade, and at prices ranging from the highest to the lowest, fully justify the widespread celebrity the house has attained. We may add, this business is the oldest of its kind in Blackburn, and has always been carried on in the same particular lines, i.e. as tailor and stay-maker.

Meadowcroft & Law, Chemists, Mineral Water Manufacturers, &c., Pump Street, Blackburn.—Among the notable industries that modern advancement in knowledge and practical science has given birth to, there are few that stand forth more prominently than mineral water manufacture, and few that have made greater progress than the same. The splendid condition of development in which this trade now exists is admirably illustrated at the well-known establishment of Messrs. Meadowcroft & Law, in Pump Street, Blackburn, where the very latest phases of improvement in the workings and facilities of the industry are exemplified. The important house under notice was founded in 1876 by Mr. W. Meadowcroft, and was subsequently acquired by its present proprietor, Mr. James Law, under whose able and thoroughly practical administration it has been increasingly successful. The premises occupied in Pump Street are of very large extent, being 100 feet long by 70 feet wide, and three storeys in height. Indeed they are the most extensive and commodious premises devoted to mineral water manufacture in this district. Their equipment is in the highest degree effective, and comprises the newest and best patents in machinery and appliances designed to place an industry of this nature upon the soundest basis in the matter of productive capability and economy. With improved steam corking and filling-machines, and various other labour-saving contri-

PUMP STREET WORKS, BLACKBURN.

vances, the firm ensure a rapid and well-sustained output, and they secure this without the slightest sacrifice of quality in their productions. As a matter of fact increased care is bestowed upon the making of the various mineral waters; and nothing in this whole establishment is more noteworthy or pleasingly impressive than the unceasing precautions taken to ensure perfect cleanliness in each and every department of the works. We need hardly add that these precautions have their looked for and excellent result; and Messrs. Meadowcroft and Law's mineral waters are produced amid surroundings of neatness, tidiness, and absolute cleanliness which leave no room for objection by even the most fastidious. The character and quality of these waters need no vindication here. They possess and well maintain a standard reputation, and have won the general favour and confidence by consistent excellence in purity and palatable nature. All this is clearly traceable to the enterprise of the firm in raising their productive facilities to the highest level of efficiency; and now, with a large and handsome establishment, a costly plant, and a numerous staff of thoroughly experienced hands, this house is fully qualified to lead the mineral water trade in the vicinity of Blackburn. The firm's connection is extensive and valuable, ranging over a radius of about twenty miles around this busy town; and Mr. James Law's careful and yet amply energetic management of the business is of a character tending to continuously enhance its well-merited prosperity.

Samuel Hodgson, Chair, Sofa, and Cabinet Manufacturer, 5, Cort Street, Market Place, Blackburn.—Established in the year 1874, in Larkhill, Mr. Hodgson on account of increasing trade was compelled in 1884 to remove to his present more commodious premises. These occupy a spacious building of three storeys in height with a large timber yard in the rear which is completely filled with the valuable woods used in the trade. The front warehouse has a very attractive appearance from the street and displays to advantage a splendid stock of the firm's products in household furniture of all kinds. In a large show room in the rear is a splendid stock of wood, brass, and iron bedsteads, hair, flock, spring, and straw mattresses, feather and wool bedding, blankets, sheets, quilts, &c.; and adjacent to this show room is another where are displayed all kinds of Brussels, tapestry, and Kidderminster carpets, oil-cloths, linoleums, mattings, rugs, curtains, &c. The works are equipped in first-rate style with all the most approved appliances. The trade of the firm, in which twenty men are employed, is very extensive, and the business connection which reaches all over north-east Lancashire is of the most influential order. Mr. Hodgson is a gentleman of long experience and thorough practical knowledge and the excellent quality of the products, the artistic taste displayed in the designs of the high class furniture and the exceedingly moderate prices charged in every department have helped him to gain the well-deserved position he now enjoys. Mr. Hodgson is a well-known gentleman and possessing an agreeable obliging manner and a reputation for the honourable methods by which he has won the confidence of the people, he is much respected by all with whom he meets whether in connection with business or matters affecting the well-being of his fellows.

Rakestraw & Son, Tailors and Woollen Drapers, 7, Town Hall Buildings, Exchange Street, Blackburn.—Among the high-class tailoring establishments of Blackburn, certainly one of the best known and most widely patronised is that conducted under the style of "Rakestraw & Son," at the address given above. The business was founded as far back as the year 1858, by Mr. William Beardsworth, at premises in Corporation Street. In 1879 the concern passed into the hands of Messrs. Rakestraw & Son, who removed the business to the present address. The elder Mr. Rakestraw died in 1888, and now the sole principal is his son, Mr. Joseph Charles Rakestraw, a gentleman who is deservedly popular both as a tradesman and a citizen. The trade of the establishment is all "bespoke," and the numerous patrons of the house include a large number of the gentry of Blackburn and the surrounding districts. The premises are spacious, and admirably adapted to the purposes of the trade, and the showrooms, &c., are suitably fitted up; whilst the workrooms are commodious, and well lighted and ventilated. The stock is very extensive and diversified, and exceedingly choice, including all the finest goods from the West of England, French, and Scotch markets, embracing all the latest designs and patterns that have become popular, and is certainly unsurpassed for general excellence. Only first-class cutters and skilled workmen are employed at this emporium, and the most careful supervision is exercised over every department; consequently, garments are produced which, for style, fit, and workmanship, cannot be excelled. It is perhaps needless to add, after our foregoing observations—and yet it is but bare justice we should—that not only has the concern gained a widespread and influential connection, but it has acquired a high reputation throughout the Blackburn and surrounding district; and the honourable and straightforward lines upon which the business is carried on has secured for the worthy proprietor (Mr. J. C. Rakestraw) the goodwill and respect of his numerous patrons.

Miss M. A. Duckworth, Confectioner, &c., 7, Corporation Street, Blackburn.—One of the oldest and best known houses in Blackburn engaged in the confectionery trade is that of Miss M. A. Duckworth, the sole proprietor, the business having been founded by Miss Derbyshire some forty-two years ago, and transferred to the present owner in 1883. The front shop is well appointed, and has an attractive appearance. The bakery also contains a most efficient working plant for the production of all kinds of fancy bread, cakes, &c. An excellent supply of fancy bread, cakes, confectionery of all kinds, sweetmeats, &c., are invariably kept on hand in the front shop, where the display attracts considerable public appreciation. The house is held in high repute for the well-sustained excellence of all its productions, a fact readily understood by reason of all the ingredients used being of the best and finest quality obtainable, added to which the skilled labour employed necessarily produces goods of such a quality and flavour as to merit public favour in a marked degree, and it is gratifying to record that these efforts are so largely reciprocated. The business is admirably conducted, and a large better-class trade carried on among the residents of the locality.

F. Cowburn, Umbrella Manufacturer, Exchange Flags, Blackburn.—This business was founded about thirteen years ago at the above address, where the proprietor occupies premises that are well adapted to the requirements of the trade. Mr. Cowburn combines the trade of hairdresser with that of umbrella manufacturer, and the shop is therefore arranged with due regard to the two branches. One portion is devoted to the display of all descriptions of umbrellas and walking-sticks, while on the other may be seen a choice assortment of hair pomades, brushes, combs, fancy goods, and a host of other items of toilet requisites too numerous to mention. In addition to the above branches he does a good-class business in silk and felt hats and boys' caps, &c. Mr. Cowburn has long been noted for the superior quality and durability of the umbrellas he supplies, and while he has devoted special attention to excellence of manufacture and material, he has also managed to combine with these a very reasonable scale of prices that will compare very favourably with those charged at any establishment in the trade. A large business is done in re-covering and repairing umbrellas of all kinds. He has suitable saloons fitted in the most modern and improved style with hair-brushing machinery, &c., and in every detail equipped for carrying on a first-class trade. In both departments of the business a great amount of success has been achieved, and this may be greatly attributed to the marked energy and ability with which the proprietor has conducted the management.

James Whittle, Wholesale Jeweller, &c., 48, Victoria Buildings, Market Place, Blackburn.—This well-known gentleman commenced business in 1874, originally at No. 4, Northgate, and in consequence of its rapid development he removed to No. 42, King William Street, and again, for the same reason, to the present extensive and commodious premises. The latter comprise a large and handsome double shop, with fine plate-glass frontage, which Mr. Whittle put in new a few years ago, at the same time greatly enlarging and improving the premises. Above the shop are three spacious and well-appointed workrooms, together with extensive warehouse accommodation, and all the accessories of a large and thoroughly-organised establishment. The shop is fitted up in a very superior style ; the fixtures and appointments are at once elegant and substantial, and the decorations are in good taste and in admirable keeping with the high tone of the establishment. The stock of goods, as becomes a business of this magnitude, is very large and comprehensive, replete with all the best features of the various lines engaged in, and thoroughly representative of the trade in all its branches, embracing as it does a large and varied assortment of gold and silver plate of the most skilful workmanship and refined beauty, gold and silver watches by the most eminent makers, jewellery, precious stones, optical instruments, barometers, spectacles, clocks, timepieces, and many chaste and elegant designs in gold and silver plate suitable for presentation ; indeed, a special feature of the business is the designing, making, and engraving of challenge cups, medals, &c., and it is interesting to note that Mr. Whittle designed, made, and engraved the silver trowel and mallet with which in 1888 the Prince of Wales laid the foundation stone of the Technical Schools at Blackburn, Mr. Whittle's design being selected by the Corporation out of a large number sent in from all parts of the country. Amongst the many valuable Cups, &c., that Mr. Whittle has supplied within the past few years may be mentioned—the East Lancashire Football Charity Cup ; the Lancashire Amateur Cricket Association Challenge Cup ; the King Wilkinson Challenge Cup, supplied to the order of W. King Wilkinson, Esq., of Middlewood, who presented it to the North-East Lancashire Cyclists' Association for annual competition ; the Feilden Challenge Cup, presented to the Witton Football Club by Lieut.-General Feilden, of Witton Park, to be competed for annually at the athletic festival of the club. The designs of these trophies were all original, and were selected in severe competition with some of the leading houses in the country. Half a dozen skilled and experienced workmen are employed in the various departments. Mr. Whittle has a first-class business connection, and numbers among his patrons many of the aristocracy and gentry of the county, and the leading merchants, manufacturers, and residents of Blackburn and the neighbourhood. The business in every department receives the strict personal attention of the proprietor, and is conducted throughout with marked ability, energy, and enterprise. Mr. James Whittle is well known and highly esteemed in Blackburn for his long and honourable connection with the town, and his earnest endeavours in promoting the best interest of its commerce, trade, and industries.

E. Cottam, Cigar and Tobacco Merchant, Station Road, Blackburn.—One of the most celebrated cigar and tobacco divans in the town is that conducted by Mr. Edward Cottam, the sole proprietor, the business having been founded by him fifteen years ago. The mart has a fine street frontage, and is centrally situated. The stock, too, is heavy, and of the best and finest quality extant. Conspicuous among the specialities for which the house has a high reputation all over the town is Cottam's celebrated "Mascotte" brand of cigars, 18s. per hundred ; and in Havanas the regular stock is only bought from houses of established repute. They can always be relied upon, and especially the Intimidads, Cavanas, Murias, Carolinas, and La Glorias. Besides these there are also heavy weights in Mexicans, all of which are well known and remarkably good cigars. In foreign goods, bona fide, there are also specialities in Maturins, a large cigar with a free draw ; and San Felipe, a medium size and delicious to smoke. Then there is the Santago, an exceedingly choice little cigar, perfectly made, and entirely of Havana leaf. Morena, too, is a very choice smoke, made of Brazilian and Havana. All these and many others on hand are particularly suitable for presents. They can be had singly, in small quantities, or in half boxes or whole boxes. In cigarettes, also, all the most fashionable brands are kept, together with a good selection of briars, shilling briars, meerschaum and cherrywood pipes, Broseley clays, &c., and a host of most useful pocket requisites for smokers. In tobaccos the stock is equally good and select, all the loose and fancy tobaccos being shown in grand display, as well as all the ordinary shags, cut cake, cut Cavendish, and such like besides ; at any rate, all the tobaccos on hand, apart from the English and Scotch houses, are all well worth inspection by connoisseurs and the trade generally. The stock is kept in excellent order, and a superior window display is made, which albeit attracts considerable public attention. The trade is extensive, and well established among the better class of customers. Mr. Cottam is a gentleman of great experience in the business, and highly respected in local trade circles.

W. H. Cunliffe, Decorator, &c., Paper Hangings, Paint, Oil Colour, Varnish, and Brush Merchant, 21, Church Street, and 4, Thwaites Arcade, Blackburn.—The various departments of the extensive business carried on by Mr. W. H. Cunliffe, Decorator, Paper Hangings, Paint, Oil, Colour, Varnish, and Brush Merchant, &c., at his two establishments, 21, Church Street, and 4, Thwaites Arcade, present many features of more than ordinary interest, and form one of the most thoroughly representative establishments of the kind in this town or district. The business dates back in its foundation to the year 1866, when it was established by the present proprietor at 13, King Street, and in consequence of its rapid development and the necessity for increased accommodation, the present premises were acquired in 1873, or rather the site upon which they stand, for the year following the premises were rebuilt and large workrooms added. They now comprise a large and handsome shop with exceptionally fine plate-glass frontage, also extensive warehouse accommodation, office and counting house, having telephonic communication (No. 173), and all the accessories of a large and thoroughly organized establishment. The stock of goods, as becomes a business of this magnitude, is very large and comprehensive, being replete with all the best features of the various lines engaged in, and fully representative of the trade in all its branches, embracing as it does all kinds of high-class decorations, paints, oils, varnishes, white lead, English and foreign paper hangings. The stock of these is exceptionally large and for variety, improved design and excellence of quality cannot be surpassed. Mr. Cunliffe is also a very large importer of room and picture frame mouldings, brushes of every description, decorators' and artists' materials ; and he also does a large business as a decorator and manufacturer of picture frames, looking-glass and window cornices, &c. ; he is also an extensive dealer in high-class pictures and works of art, large connoisseurs and institutions having made purchases from him. Decorating most of the churches and chapels and public buildings and mansions in the town, London, Scotland, and all parts of the country, decorative painting is a leading speciality, and the shops and show rooms contain many beautiful specimens of this art, which well display in every detail of design, execution and finish the superior skill and talent employed in this establishment. The branch shop at 4, Thwaites Arcade is devoted chiefly to the art department of the business, and contains a large stock of colours, paints, brushes, architects', artists', and decorators' materials, &c. Mr. Cunliffe employs altogether about forty skilled and experienced workmen, and has the largest and most influential connection of the kind in Blackburn and the neighbourhood. The business in every department receives the strict personal attention of the proprietor and is conducted throughout with marked ability, energy and enterprise. Mr. W. H. Cunliffe occupies a prominent and influential position in business circles, and is well known and highly esteemed for his long and honourable connection with this town and district.

J. Ireland, Bootmaker, &c., Northgate, Blackburn.—An old and well-known house in the branch of British industry above referred to is that of Mr. J. Ireland, the sole proprietor, the business having been originated by Mr. Higham over half a century ago in the town and carried on at the above address for the past twenty-seven years. The stock held comprises a splendid assortment of general and fancy boots, shoes, and slippers, the quality of which can be guaranteed second to none. A distinctive feature of the stock is to be found in dress boots and shoes, a large variety being invariably kept on hand ; among which ladies' French kids and satins abound in profusion. These goods are specially well worth a visit by matinee-goers, and others. In ladies' ordinary wear, too, there are some first-class goods in substantial walking boots, durable, easy to wear, and elegant in appearance. Then again in house boots the stock is equally good and select, the style and finish of Mr. Ireland's boots and shoes for ladies and children being such as to spread their renown all over the neighbourhood. Slippers there are in all the fashionable materials and best make, while in point of design and finish these goods are equal to any offered to the public by the local houses. In gents' goods, also, the winter boots shown are specially noteworthy, and such as must prove invaluable to those who have to spend much of their time out of doors in rainy weather. All the boots and shoes in this section of the stock are perfect in fit, as, indeed, are all the others, elegant in appearance and substantial in make. In the measure department special regard is had to the structure of the foot, whereby ease and comfort in walking is insured, bespoke orders being promptly attended to as one of the specialities for which the house has a high reputation. Repairs, too, are neatly and promptly executed, the best English tanned leather only being used, the work entrusted to skilled workmen under the supervision of the proprietor. The business is well organised and carried on with tact, push, and energy. The trade extensive and chiefly confined to the neighbourhood. Mr. Ireland is a practical craftsman and a gentleman of the highest trade status.

K

James Turner, Contractor for Removing Furniture, &c., to all parts of the world, King Street, Blackburn.—Among those modern developments of business enterprise which have added so largely to the conveniences of life at the present day must be reckoned the work and calling of him who contracts for the removal of furniture and household effects from one place to another, and thus relieves mankind of a vast amount of trouble and anxiety that would otherwise attend him whenever he might be constrained to change the place of his abode. Every important town in the United Kingdom has now one or more of such contractors, and at Blackburn the business is most creditably represented by Mr. James· Turner of King Street. Mr. Turner commenced his operations in this line as far back as 1868, and his establishment, which has always been located in King Street, is well and favourably known at the present time to a large and widespread circle of patrons. His business is certainly the largest of its kind in Blackburn, and has steadily increased from the first—a circumstance due to able and painstaking management and the faithful and satisfactory carrying out of all contracts entered into by the house. The premises occupied are the Old Barracks, in King Street, and of large extent, and arranged with excellent judgment to afford warehouse accommodation for a great quantity of furniture, goods or effects. In the removing of furniture and other movable property from any one place to any other place, however great the distance, Mr. Turner has proved himself to be possessed of admirable facilities. He has made an exhaustive study of the ways and means in this matter, and the result is that he can accomplish the most extensive removals by road, rail, or sea, without packing, and deliver the furniture, &c., at its specified destination in absolutely the same order and condition as that in which it was entrusted to his care. The many times he has demonstrated his ability to do all this has inspired general confidence in his resources ; and by the recommendation of those who have patronised him with satisfactory results his business has been continuously increased. Mr. Turner now keeps in operation eight large and improved pantechnicon vans for furniture removals, and these can be despatched with their loads to any distance, by road or rail, as may be most expedient. The loading of the vans and the unloading of the same at the points of departure and arrival is performed by men of special training and ability in such work, and Mr. Turner's men have won excellent opinions for their skill, care, and civility, in the discharge of their duties. We may mention that special care is bestowed upon the removal of pianofortes, wines, china and earthenware ; and persons having valuable and perishable articles of this description to move generally find that it pays much better to call in the aid of a contractor of thorough practical experience rather that to attempt the removal without such assistance. Breakages are unknown when Mr. Turner's men have the work in hand. Besides the vans above referred to the house has ten lurries and eight carts for general work, and all the appliances and requisites for a business of this kind upon the largest scale. Mr. Turner, who is well known and much esteemed in Blackburn, devotes his attention most untiringly to the management of his successful business, and is assiduous in his efforts to afford every satisfaction to the large and influential connection whose support he enjoys.

Mrs. Slater, Abdominal and Surgical Belt and Truss Maker, 13, Victoria Street, Blackburn.—This business, which is the foremost of its kind in this district of England, was established in Accrington in 1878 by Mrs. Slater, the present proprietress, who removed to her present address in 1886 The premises consist of a comfortably-furnished consulting room on the ground floor, with a spacious workroom on the floor above. Of all kinds of surgical supports, Mrs. Slater has specimens in her handsome consulting room, as well as of special appliances for deformities, spinal supports, chest expanders, elastic stockings, knee-caps, &c. Having won the confidence of the faculty, who have acknowledged her appliances to be the best of the kind ever brought before the public, Mrs. Slater does an extensive business, which requires the services of several workers. It should be mentioned that she has the assistance of her husband, who is in attendance for males in the consulting room daily from 6 p.m. to 8 p.m., she being in attendance during the hours of from 10 a.m. to 6 p.m. daily except on Mondays, when she attends to other matters, including her engagement at the Literary Institution, Manchester Road, Burnley, where she has been attending for the last three years. Amongst numerous testimonials received by this firm, space here will only permit of one being inserted, which we give as follows :—" 45, Seymour Street, Portman Square, London, W., October, 1882. I am greatly pleased with the Abdominal and Prolapsus Uteri Combination Belt as made by Mrs. Slater, of Accrington, and consider it admirably adapted for those cases for which it is intended, as well as those of weakness of the Abdominal Parieties from any cause. The workmanship is all that can be desired. OSMAN VINCENT, F.R.C.S. ED. ; M.R.C.S., A.K.C., &c." Possessing a quiet, sympathetic manner, Mrs. Slater is much liked by her numerous supporters, many of whom, as well as medical gentlemen in all parts of Lancashire and in distant parts of England, regard her as a benefactress who has well earned the high place she enjoys in the esteem of thousands of sufferers from physical weakness. Mr. Slater is an agreeable, courteous gentleman, and much respected by a large circle of influential gentlemen in and around Lancashire.

Henry Hindle, Chemist and Druggist, 66, King Street, Blackburn.—Half a century ago there was established by the late Mr. Richard Baines that splendid chemist and druggist business now in the hands of Mr. Henry Hindle, 66, King Street, Blackburn. Where Mr. Baines commenced business was on the opposite side of the street from the present premises : the removal was made in the year 1841. Mr. Hindle served his apprenticeship as a chemist and druggist with Mr. Baines, and in 1865 they joined partnership, and carried on a most successful business together. Mr. Baines died in 1886, leaving his partner, Mr. Hindle, sole proprietor. The shop is well fitted with all the usual appointments of a chemist and druggist's establishment. There are two counters for serving and two fine show windows. The stocks are extensive, and composed of all the drugs embraced in the British Pharmacopœia, with a number of proprietary articles and patent medicines, as well as perfumes, toilet soaps, and the thousand and one etceteras that make a druggist premises at once attractive and imposing. A warehouse of three storeys, with cellars used for stores, packing and making up the wholesale orders, make the premises commodious and complete. In the retail department the most scrupulous care is observed in selecting pure drugs for dispensing purposes, and the same care is taken in making up prescriptions, this establishment being largely recommended by the medical practitioners of the town, relying on the accuracy of their proportions as well as on the purity of the drugs dispensed. The wholesale trade extends all over Blackburn and district, a large trade being done in both departments. Several of the members of Mr. Hindle's family give him able assistance in the management of the business, which is carried on with great regularity and in perfect order, leaving the principal to devote a portion of his time to the public service. Mr. Hindle was a town councillor for nine years, being first elected in 1876, and retired from the representation in 1885. He is very popular in Blackburn with the general public, and is held in great regard by the leading members of the medical profession of the district.

John Waring, Tailor and Outfitter, 2, Astleygate, Blackburn.—A celebrated house in the tailoring trade is that conducted by the gentleman above referred to, who was for some time a pupil of the illustrious firm of Edward Minister & Son, of London, tailors and habit-makers to her Majesty. This flourishing business was established by him near the present address about ten years ago, and removed to the premises now occupied in 1884. A particularly good display of high-class boys' ready-made suits is shown in materials suited to the present season. The staple trade is in the bespoke department. To meet the daily increasing trade in this line, a large and varied stock of piece goods from the best known looms in the country are always kept on hand, such as Angolas, Cheviots, Cashmeres, homespuns, Meltons, serges, flannels, West of England trouserings and coatings, vicunas, and all the latest novelties in Irish tweeds, &c., the quality of which can be guaranteed. Over the shop is the showroom, well filled with clothing and piece goods of every description, and intending patrons visiting the establishment will meet with every courtesy and attention, though merely wishing to view the various specialities on hand. A speciality of the house is ladies' jackets and other garments, habits, &c., and the principal is unexcelled as to fit and workmanship. The workshops are in Mincing Lane, commodious and well-appointed, and here at least a dozen picked tradesmen are permanently employed in this branch of industry, Mr. Waring carefully superintending every detail of work. Thorough workmanship marks the various garments, and proves their general design and commercial value to be of no mean order. The custom is extensive, and well established among the better class of customers. The proprietor is a gentleman practically acquainted with all the details of the tailor's art, and esteemed by all with whom he has business relations.

James Hargreaves, Wholesale Tobacconist and Cigar Merchant, 36, King William Street, Blackburn.—This business was established by the present proprietor in the year 1862, and carried on at No. 2, Church Street for fifteen years with great success, until it completely outgrew the capacity of the premises, compelling Mr. Hargreaves in 1877 to remove to his present address, having purchased the property in 1876. Here the reputation of the house has continued to extend, and at present Mr. Hargreaves owns one of the most extensive concerns in this line of business in the country. The premises are of large extent, consisting of a handsome front shop with store-rooms above and spacious warehouses in the rear. The sale-shop, with handsomely fitted offices, is admirably arranged to suit the business, enabling the assistants to handle goods and execute orders in a most expeditious manner. Including the principal the trade of the firm requires the services of four travellers, a goodly number of packers, book-keepers, horses, &c., and the business continues to grow year by year. Mr. Hargreaves is a keen sportsman, an old member of the P.F.H., rides good cattle, and is generally to the fore when hounds go fast. Although not taking a prominent part in political matters, Mr. Hargreaves takes a warm interest in any worthy object to which his attention is drawn, and he is known as having been one of the prime movers in establishing the High School for girls in Preston Road, an educational institution which has been a marked success and promises to be of great value to the town.

Cash & Co., Hat Manufacturers, 53, King William Street, Blackburn, and 55, St. James Street, Burnley.—One of the most eminent Blackburn houses in its line is that of the firm above referred to, and by whom the business was founded in 1885. Mr. Oldham is the managing partner, and under that gentleman's judicious administration the house has already come to the front rank of the local hat trade, apart from their claim to the public confidence by reason of the surpassing excellence of the goods offered to the public. Their works are situated at Denton, and contain a most efficient plant, including all the most improved machinery and appliances for the manufacture of hats of every description; and in addition the firm employ regularly a full staff of experienced hands in this branch of industry. The stock held by the King William Street house is large and comprehensive, and consists not only of hats and caps of every description, but also of umbrellas, which are manufactured by the firm in large quantities. These umbrellas are in silk and best Gloria, the new warranted covers, and other fabrics, all on Paragon frames, and furnished with well-selected handles, &c.; in fact this line of their stock is particularly

well worth a visit, all umbrellas being offered at wholesale prices. This is also an important and distinctive feature of the hat and cap department, every item being marked at wholesale figures. Their silk hats are the best possible obtainable value in the trade. Attractive in shape, substantial in make, and possessed of many excellences in wear-resisting qualities, it is not a matter of surprise that these hats should be in general demand among the inhabitants of the town. In felts, too, they do an extensive handling, their productions in this line being noted for their unique fit, shape, style, and general appearance; and in addition every hat is warranted of the best workmanship and material. In caps, likewise, they also do a large turn-over, their design and finish being all that could possibly be desired in this line of British industry. The trade is very extensive and well-established throughout the town and neighbourhood. The firm members are gentlemen of the greatest enterprise and business ability, and held in high esteem by all with whom they have commercial relations. The Burnley branch, at 55, St. James Street, is under the same judicious management, and corresponds in every detail with the Blackburn establishment in prices, quality, and general excellence.

James Welch, Watch and Clock Maker, &c., 55, King William Street, opposite the Town Hall, Blackburn.—A premier house in the watch, clock, and jewellery trade is that of Mr. James Welch, the sole proprietor, the business having been founded by him at the address mentioned over twenty years ago. An attractive display of all the usual specialities of the trade is made in the spacious window of the establishment, and an equally large and comprehensive stock is seen within, the general quality of which is guaranteed. The strong part of the goods on hand is found in watches, gold and silver, in all sizes for ladies and gentlemen, perfect in mechanism, and warranted accurate time-keepers. The clocks include a large assortment of ormolus, marble-cased drawing-and dining-room and hall clocks, in handsomely carved cases, with clear dials, and so well-adjusted mechanism as to render them accurate time-keepers in all seasons and climates. Gold and silver jewellery, silver and electro-plated goods, also constitute a speciality for which the house has a high reputation all over the neighbourhood. The whole of the stock is kept in thorough business-like order and conveniently arranged for the inspection of customers, to whom the greatest courtesy is at all times extended to inspect the specialities on hand. Repairing in all its branches is undertaken, a full staff of picked tradesmen being regularly employed in connection with this branch of the business—Mr. Welch carefully superintending all work executed under the prestige of the house, and generally directing the organization of the business. The custom is extensive, and well established among the better class of patrons. The proprietor is a practical craftsman, and a gentleman who bestows unremitting attention to every branch of his business in order to execute all orders to the entire satisfaction of all those who may honour him with their commands.

Eardley Walker, Merchant Tailor, Northgate, Blackburn.—This flourishing business has been established about seventeen years, during which time it has made exceptionally marked progress, and now ranks among the foremost of the kind in Lancashire. The premises comprise a large and handsomely-fitted shop, having a commanding corner position, the appearance of which is prepossessing, and much enhanced by the manner in which the stock is displayed. There is a very choice assortment of piece goods, including all the best class of tweeds, Meltons, woollens, &c., of every description, all of these being the production of the most renowned manufacturing firms. Ready-made goods also form a very great feature, and the windows are filled with a fine display of suits for gentlemen and juveniles, and a variety of goods incidental to this class of trade. It should be particularly noticed that the firm sell goods of their own manufacture only. Above the show-rooms there are spacious work-rooms, where no less than sixty hands are employed in various branches of tailoring, and including many that have been specially selected from among the most skilled and experienced artizans. The whole of the work is carried on under careful supervision, and nothing is omitted that may tend to ensure perfection of material and make. The firm have thus acquired a first-class reputation, and have developed an enormous trade, which extends to all parts of the surrounding neighbourhood. To such an extent has the business increased that the scope of the firm's operations has been enlarged by the opening of a branch establishment at 40, Church Street, which comprises a fine corner shop, elegantly fitted and stocked in the same complete and attractive manner that characterizes the Northgate depôt. No manufacturing is done at the branch, all this work being executed under the immediate superintendence of the principal at the establishment in Northgate. The business is very ably conducted, and the progress made, together with the pre-eminent position acquired, reflect great credit upon the enterprising proprietor.

J. Allan, Optician, 26A, King William Street, and 128, Montague Street, Blackburn.—This business was established in 1886 by Messrs. Shaw Brothers, whose manager was Mr. Allan. In 1887 Messrs. Shaw retired from the concern, which was at once taken over by Mr. Allan, and he has already secured an excellent and thriving connection. The premises consist of a single shop with one large plate-glass window, which is well arranged and fitted up, the valuable stock consisting of spectacles of every description, opera and field glasses in great variety and price, magnifying glasses, barometers and thermometers of all kinds and for all purposes; theodolites and other surveying instruments; drawing instruments in very considerable variety and at all prices; as well as a miscellaneous assortment of other goods for scientific and other purposes. Mr. Allan devotes special attention to spectacles, of which an exceedingly large and extremely varied assortment is always on hand. His long scientific experience is of the greatest value to his large circle of patrons. Mr. Allan, who also attends the Market Hall, Darwen, every Monday, Friday, and Saturday, has found it necessary to caution the public against hawkers of spectacles, who represent themselves as eye doctors and oculists, for the purpose of swindling customers into paying four or five times the value of the article they purchase. His glasses are accurately fitted up to remedy or aid any of the following defects of vision: myopia, or short sight; hypermetropia, or long sight; presbyopia, or old sight; asthenopia, or weak sight; muscœ volitantes, or opacities in the vitreous chamber; power lost after operation for cataract; astigmatism, or irregular sight; strabismus, or squint; and the numerous other impairments of sight. Gold and silver spectacles and eye glasses are made to order, and repairs of every description promptly attended to and neatly executed. Mr. Allan also devotes attention to the subject of artificial eyes—which he keeps in stock—and has been very successful in replacing, in appearance at least, the loss of that important organ. He does a considerable business, and employs a couple of assistants, the whole establishment being under his special supervision and management, while the scientific department is entirely under his personal care and particular attention.

James Haydock, Reed & Heald Manufacturer and Mill Furnisher, Randal Street Works, Blackburn.—This well-known and old established firm was commenced by Mr. Haydock in 1863. The present premises are known as the Randal Street Works, covering a large area of ground and are two storeys in height. They are equipped in first-rate style with all the most approved machinery for the production of Reeds, Healds, and Heald Yarns. Healds are made for all kinds of fancy weaving, any number of shafts. The ground floor of the building, which has a handsome office, is devoted to the reed-making and

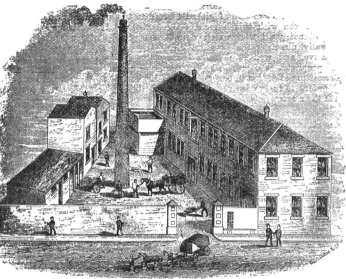

doubling of heald yarns, the upper flat being devoted to the manufacture of healds, &c. The machines, of which there are a large number, are all by the foremost makers. The trade of the firm extends all over Lancashire, a large business being done by Mr. Haydock as a leather merchant and general mill furnisher. The excellence of the reeds and healds produced by this firm has gained a high reputation in the busy mills of Blackburn and the surrounding districts, and through this, and the honourable methods that have always characterised the management of the business, Mr. Haydock enjoys the esteem and confidence of his supporters.

Rufus Middlebrook, Hatter, &c., 2, King William Street, Blackburn.—Mr. R. Middlebrook is a well-known hat and cap manufacturer, with premises at No. 2, King William Street, Blackburn. The business was established about 1830 in these premises by Mr. John Umpleby, who gathered together an excellent trading connection. He was succeeded, in the year 1880, by the present proprietor, by whom the concern has been conducted on the old lines with the greatest success. The premises comprise a large double shop, with a frontage of about 30 feet, extending backwards about 12 feet. A very attractive outside display of all kinds of superior hats and caps is made, while the interior is exceedingly well arranged and fitted up for the transaction of a large business. The fixtures are all of the most excellent character, well made and most suitably arranged. A very large and varied stock of goods is always on hand, consisting of a first-class assortment of hats and caps of the latest make and fashion, and supplied by the best houses in the trade. The excellence of the goods accounts for the large and thriving business which is done by Mr. Middlebrook, only goods of undoubted quality being kept on the premises. The whole trade is under the careful personal management of the proprietor himself, by whom the greatest care and attention is given to the wants of his large and increasing circle of customers and friends.

Mrs. Sarah Fowler & Sons, Silk Mercers and General Drapers, Preston New Road, Blackburn.—This business was established thirty years ago by Mrs. Sarah Fowler, the present head of the firm, which for the last fifteen years has comprised this lady and her two sons, Messrs. Edward and Frank Fowler. Mrs. Fowler & Sons built their present premises at Preston New Road, and have been in their occupation for four years. The establishment consists of a large block of stone building, reaching to a height of five floors, and has a large and massive frontage of fifty feet, with three heavy plate-glass windows. The shop is beautifully fitted up, and furnished with two long counters. An oak staircase leads to the show-rooms, stock-rooms, and work-rooms, situated on the other four floors. A large trade is conducted here in the various departments of silk mercery, general drapery, dressmaking and millinery. The firm also act as funeral undertakers, and supply every requisite in this line. A rich and valuable stock is held in general lines, including drapery, curtains, lace, quilts, eiderdown goods, leather fancy merchandise, bags, satchels, &c. A special feature is made of costumes, mantles, ladies' underclothing and family mourning; and, including milliners, dressmakers, and other auxiliaries, a staff of fifty hands are employed. This is a business where all the features of refined taste and reliable goods are present in a very marked degree. Mrs. Fowler is possessed of excellent taste and discernment. She is ably supported by her two sons; and the successful position of this business affords a fine illustration of what can be accomplished by harmonious working, sound judgment, and thorough mercantile capacity.

Wm. Pinder, Glass and Porcelain Merchant, 43, King William Street, Blackburn.—This business was founded over thirty-five years ago by the present proprietor, who then occupied premises in Church Street. About twenty years since the continued increase and development in the trade necessitated removal to the address as above. Mr. Pinder now occupies a large shop, which presents a more than usually attractive appearance. The ground floor forms the show-room, and here there is a very choice assortment of high-class goods of all kinds incidental to porcelain, glass, and earthenware. The display in this show-room, both in the windows and generally throughout, is particularly noticeable, the goods being admirably arranged, and including a very large proportion of the most artistic and valuable items of the stock. The upper floors are used as warehouses and store-rooms, and these are stocked in the same complete manner. The premises are fitted with a powerful hoist for the upper floors, and all the arrangements are upon a similar complete scale. Among the chief items of the stock, which is of far too comprehensive a nature for detailed mention, some of the world-renowned products of such firms as Minton, Copeland, Wedgwood, Worcester, Wittman & Roth, Thos. Webb & Sons, form noticeable features. All the goods are of the best class of manufacture, a very high standard of excellence having been maintained throughout. A large trade is done, not only in the immediate vicinity, but also generally in all parts of the locality in and around Blackburn. One of the special features of the business consists of fitting up and lending all descriptions of table requisites for banquets, suppers, &c., on hire, a large stock of goods being always kept in reserve for this purpose. The management is characterized by great energy and enterprise, and to this the success is chiefly due.

James Garstang, Wholesale Tobacconist, Market Place, and 2, King William Street, Blackburn.—Mr. Garstang commenced business about a quarter of a century ago, at No. 2, King Street, and in 1883 opened a branch shop in the Market Place, and has long conducted a most extensive and prosperous trade, embracing the whole of the departments of the business of a general tobacconist and dealer in fancy goods. The premises include an extensive shop, with a frontage of about 40 feet, and a large store-room above, which is filled with a large assortment of goods. The interior of the shop is exceedingly well arranged for business, while the fixtures are in the best taste, giving a most effective aspect to the whole. The window is always "dressed" in the best style, and a very fine display of tobaccos and fancy articles, &c., is at all times produced. The stock consists of all the most popular favourite tobaccos in the market, and the best known and celebrated brands of cigars and cigarettes, while there is a most extensive and varied assortment of all kinds of pipes, from the very best makers in clay, wood, and meerschaum, as well as the fancy goods so generally affected by lovers of the "weed," including tobacco pouches, cigar and cigarette cases, holders, &c., &c. Mr. Garstang's establishment is really very popular and in regular request. In every way the stock here is especially large and of a high-class character, and Mr. Garstang well deserves the large and increasing patronage he is receiving. He employs four assistants, but the whole establishment is under his own special care, attention, and superintendence, and he spares neither capital, enterprise, or energy, in order to make his business the most popular and attractive in the town. In addition to the tobacco business Mr. Garstang acts as agent for Sutton & Co., London, as well as for the Lancashire and Yorkshire, and for the London and North-Western Railway companies, in the town.

James R. Parkinson, Manufacturing Chemist and Drysalter, Ainsworth Street; Warehouse, Merchant Street, Blackburn.—This business was established in 1863 by Mr. Parkinson, who is still sole proprietor. The establishment is extensive and equipped in first-rate style with special appliances for the production of the firm's specialties. The manufactory is a model of its kind, being most tastefully fitted up and tidily kept. The specialties are famous all over Lancashire, and appreciated wherever used. The most marked of these are the Blackburn sauce and the East Lancashire sauce, made and sold since 1863, and the well-known starch improver. The Merchant Street premises are stocked with colours, oils, and chemicals, and everything belonging to the drysalter. The premises in Ainsworth Street are replete with the endless variety of articles that are demanded in a business of this character, such as drugs, perfumes, seeds, spices, and sundries. The trade extends over a considerable part of Lancashire, while some of the firm's specialties are known throughout the country. The business connection is of the most influential order, and the old-established reputation of the firm continues to be maintained and extended by the honourable methods, energy, and powers of adaptation through which it was founded. Mr. Parkinson is a well-known gentleman much respected by all who have the pleasure of meeting him, whether in connection with business or matters affecting the well-being of his fellows.

King & Blackburn, Silk Mercers and Family Drapers, Peel Buildings, Blackburn.—This concern was established thirty-five years since by Mr. William Copeland, the present title being adopted in 1876. The individual partners are Messrs. William Higham King and John Dean Blackburn. The premises consist of four floors, covering an area of 60 feet by 70 feet, with ample cellarage. The establishment is furnished with three large windows. There are six large counters; cashier's desk and a private office situated at the end of one of the shops. Messrs. King & Blackburn hold a most valuable and finely-selected stock of millinery, mantles, costumes, silks, velvets, plushes, furs, sealskin jackets, and dolmans. The household linen departments comprise a well-selected stock of table linen of every description, bed linen, &c., direct from the Belfast manufacturers; also a well-selected stock of flannels, shirting flannels, Bath coatings, blankets, Russian down and other quilts, counterpanes, sheets, sheetings, linen sheetings, pillow linens and cottons,

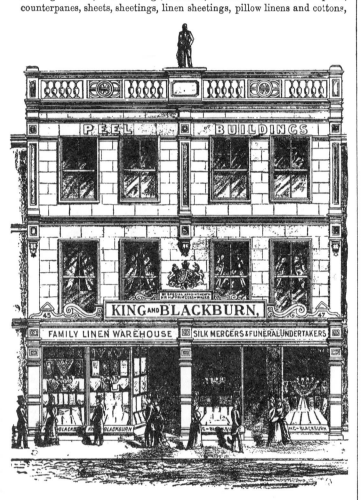

tickings, table linens, table-cloths, huckabacks, towels, Hollands, diapers, calicoes, cretonnes, tapestries, furniture prints, table-covers of all kinds, white and cream long curtains in all makes, guipure curtains, art muslins, &c. Messrs. King & Blackburn act by appointment to H.R.H. the Princess of Wales. The second floor is finely fitted out with three showrooms and stockroom, the third floor being in use as workrooms, a complement of seventy hands being employed on the establishment. The firm act as agents for Smith's Patent Metallic Sanitary Coffins, and have a high reputation as undertakers, and their establishment is recognised as being undoubtedly the best in Blackburn. The partners are men of strict business system, activity, and courtesy, and so long as Messrs. King & Blackburn continue their operations in Blackburn, the ladies of the district have a reliable and choice selection of drapery goods of every description, and have no necessity to go out of Blackburn for what they may require.

Samuel Whittaker, Painter, Paperhanger, and Decorator, 37, Preston New Road, Blackburn.—This business was originally established in 1845 as Messrs. H. Whittaker & Sons, in Church Street, where it was carried on, with the addition of the plumbing, glazing, and gas and water fitting departments, for about forty years, until the year 1885, when the present business was removed to the premises at No. 37, Preston New Road, and the name of the firm changed to Mr. Samuel Whittaker. These premises consist of a large shop, used as a commodious showroom and office, the whole measuring thirty-five feet by twenty, with a handsome plate-glass front, which affords every facility for making a most attractive display of the latest and best designs in wall papers, from the best houses in the trade. Here are displayed Lincrusta Walton, and all kinds of wall papers. The variety of these is exceedingly great, embracing the most expensive and elaborate decorative designs for halls, drawing, dining, and sitting-rooms, and staircases, as well as all the cheap and neat patterns for bedrooms, and ordinary hangings for smaller property. Specimens for house decoration are also shown, as Mr. Whittaker does a considerable amount of this class of work in the town and surrounding district. He makes a speciality, however, of ecclesiastical decoration, and several churches and other places of worship in the neighbourhood give proof of his ability in this department of artistic business. This firm are well known for their artistic sign writing. Ordinarily he employs a considerable number of hands, skilful and experienced men, while in the busy season that number is, of course, very largely increased. The firm has an excellent reputation for the high class character of its work, Mr. Whittaker only using the best material, and employing first-class operatives, in all contracts undertaken by him, while the whole is under his own personal control, supervision, and management, so that patrons may depend upon everything entrusted to his care being executed in the most satisfactory manner.

Tomlinson & Co., Tailors, 17, Aspden's Buildings (late of 78, King William Street) Blackburn.—This eminent house was founded by Mr. John Tomlinson in King William Street over thirty years ago. Subsequently the premises at the present address were occupied, and in 1880 the trade title of the house became the present designation. The firm make an excellent display of piece goods from the looms of the principal English and Scotch and Irish houses, which fully harmonises with their unique stock of new goods for the coming season, including all the latest materials suitable for ulsters, Inverness capes, overcoats, trousers, &c., liveries, &c., being lines in which they do an extensive business. The house has also a high reputation for ladies' costumes, ulsters, ladies' tailor-made jackets, riding-habits, &c., the samples of which are in every respect substantial in make, and fully abreast of the times in point of style, fit, and strength of material; in fact, the firm are showing at the present time two or three specimens that are unique in the extreme, and deserve that recognition which a large section of the public are according to them. On the first floor is the work-room, well appointed in every detail, and here are employed regularly a full staff of picked tradesmen, Messrs. Tomlinson supervising the manufacture and finish of all garments placed before the public under the prestige of the house. The business is entirely of a bespoke character and first-class in every particular, the house being worthily accredited to stand in the front ranks of the trade. The proprietors bestow the most unremitting attention to every branch of the business with the definite object of executing every order to the entire satisfaction of all those who may honour them with their commands. The firm hold the appointment of official tailors to the Cyclists' Touring Club, a position embodying a pretty sure guarantee that their clothing is of a high standard of merit, the association referred to being of a status not readily accepting any class of inferior goods. The trade is without exception of the highest class, extensive, and well established.

Thomas Critchley, Chemist and Druggist, &c., 10, King William Street, Blackburn.—One of the best known establishments in Blackburn is that of Mr. Thomas Critchley, the proprietor of the renowned "Critchley's Starch Gloss," so largely used during the last fifteen years. Mr. Critchley commenced business here in the year 1863. The premises at No. 10, King William Street are a large three-storey building, with two plate-glass windows and a frontage of about sixteen feet, extending backwards about thirty feet. The shop is well arranged and fitted for the transaction of a large business. The window display is exceedingly effective, and an extensive stock of all kinds of patent medicines, pills, drugs, &c., of the most popular and useful character are always on hand. At the back of the shop is the office, built of glass in the most attractive manner. The floors above, of the same dimensions as the shop, are occupied as storerooms for all kinds of heavy materials. Mr. Critchley is the sole inventor, patentee, and proprietor of the most useful commodity, "Starch Gloss," of which there is an enormous yearly sale through the numerous commission agents by which it is distributed throughout the country. Critchley's famous "Starch Gloss" is used in the Royal laundries. It may be used with cold as well as hot water starch; it renders soft linen impossible; it never sticks, not even to spider-web-like materials; it imparts a beautiful ivory finish and lustre to all starched fabrics, with one-half the usual labour; it also renders all fabrics non-inflammable. It is more economical; it also keeps clean much longer, hence wears better than any similar article, and it is the greatest boon ever offered to laundresses. Testimonials have been received from the chief laundress to H.R.H. the Prince of Wales and from the chief laundress to H.R.H. the Duke of Edinburgh, who speak in the highest terms of its useful properties.

James Eatough, Potato Dealer, &c., 54, Victoria Street, Blackburn.—The firm of Mr. James Eatough, potato and fruit merchant, has been familiar in Blackburn for over half a century. The business was originally established by Mr. Joseph Eatough, senior, in the year 1835, the present proprietor, Mr. James Eatough, the son of the founder, succeeding to the concern on the retirement of the latter, in the year 1863. The stores of the firm, at No. 54, Victoria Street, are a large one-storey erection, measuring thirty feet by eighteen, with the office at the entrance. They have also a large accommodation at the Lancashire and Yorkshire Railway Stations, for the reception of all consignments by rail, in the first place, and from which supplies are drawn, to meet the requirements of the Victoria Street stores, as well as for orders sent on by rail, and for deliveries, direct, to large customers in the town. Mr. Eatough generally employs four handy assistants in his business, this number, of course, being considerably extended during the pressure of the potato season. The business consists principally of the daily and weekly receipts of large consignments of potatoes, fruits, &c., and their immediate sale, but a considerable stock is also always on hand. English, Irish, Scotch, French, Continental, and American goods are at all times passing through the hands of the firm, according to the time of year. A very large trade is done yearly, extending over a very wide area. The whole is under the control and management of the proprietor himself, who has had a long and extremely varied experience in the trade. It is a business that calls for the display of the greatest care, energy, and enterprise, along with the best judgment and knowledge of details ; and in these respects Mr. Eatough is well qualified for the position he has so long filled with credit and success.

James Dewhurst, Carpet Factor, Art Cabinet Maker, Upholsterer, &c., Decorator for Balls, Private Parties, and Conversaziones, 4, Fish Lane, and 11, Lord Street West, Blackburn.—This business was established about the year 1864, in premises closely adjoining, by Mr. Charles Kilvington, and by whom an excellent trade was gathered together. He was succeeded, in the year 1876, by Mr. Dewhurst, the present proprietor, who, two years later, removed to the present address. The premises comprise a large three-storey building, with a showroom and office on the ground floor, the two upper floors being entirely used as workshops. Here a number of skilled and experienced hands are employed in cabinet and furniture making and upholstery in all the departments of the business, and a large quantity of very well-made and elegant goods are turned out, both for stock and to order. The showroom is extremely well arranged, and a very large assortment of carpets, hearthrugs, and excellent cabinet work is here displayed, as well as furniture of all kinds. Mr. Dewhurst does a very large trade in all the departments of his business, the goods supplied by him being of first-rate quality, both in material and workmanship. Another line in which Mr. Dewhurst has a large connection is in the decoration of interiors for balls, parties, and other festive occasions. The whole concern is under his own personal care and management, and his large body of customers and patrons of the highest class have their orders and commissions executed in the most prompt and satisfactory manner and at most reasonable prices. He is highly respected by his fellow-townsmen as a man of ability, energy, and enterprise.

Mrs. Mitchell, "Old Bull" Commercial and Family Hotel, Church Street, Blackburn.—To the commercial gentleman visiting distant parts the hotel is an institution of the utmost importance, and it is therefore appropriate in these reviews of our industries to make prominent mention of a thoroughly representative hotel in Blackburn. Such we have in that of the "Old Bull" Commercial and Family Hotel, which is situated in Church Street. Founded half a century ago, the "Old Bull" was rebuilt thirty years ago, and is the property of Mrs. Mitchell, who has occupied it for the last ten years. This house, which is the foremost and most popular commercial and family hotel in Blackburn, consists of a handsome square building of three storeys in height, and measuring 100 feet square. On the ground floor there are commercial room, coffee room, private sitting rooms, billiard room, four stock rooms, and bar and parlour ; the floor above having upwards of forty bedrooms, a spacious dining hall nearly occupying the whole of the upper floor. Every room is handsomely furnished, and there being twenty servants, first-class fare, moderate charges, and a most agreeable, courteous hostess, commercial gentlemen and private families at once find themselves at home in the "Old Bull," whose omnibus meets all trains for the convenience of guests coming or going.

Adley, Tolkien & Co., Chemical Manufacturers, &c., Greaves Street, Blackburn.—This well-known business was established and conducted for a great many years in London. In 1882 the firm commenced operations in Randal Street, Blackburn, and in consequence of the rapid extension of their business, built in November, 1888, the present premises in Greaves Street, which are in all respects suitably constructed, and admirably adapted to the purposes of the business engaged in. The London office of Messrs. Adley, Tolkien & Co. is situated at 14 to 20, St. Mary Axe, E.C. ; and their London works at Penton Street, Pentonville, N. The trade of this firm is world-wide, and is carried through by them in all kinds of Sizing Ingredients and Filling Materials used by Sizers, Manufacturers, Finishers, Bleachers, Calico Printers, Dyers, Polishers, &c. Their specialities embrace Sago, Rice, Tapioca, and Wheat Sizing Flour, Solid and Liquid Chloride of Zinc, Chloride of Calcium and Magnesia, China Clay, French Chalk and Barytes, Scotch and Foreign Farina, Dextrine, and Gum, Maize, Wheat, Potato and Rice Starch, Epsom and Glauber Salts, and other similar articles. Messrs. Adley, Tolkien & Co. are the Sole Makers of Lancashire "Acme" Size, and are proprietors of The Gloy Manufacturing Company, and in the operations of their concerns employ a staff of fifty assistants. This is a prosperous undertaking, most diligently and systematically conducted ; and the management of the Blackburn business is courteously and efficiently discharged by Mr. H. M. Geldart.

Thomas Briggs, Printer, Stationer, Bookbinder, and Account-Book Manufacturer, 73, Northgate, Blackburn.—Mr. Thos. Briggs commenced business some fifteen years ago, and by dint of energy, perseverance, and strict integrity, coupled with practical ability in his profession, has obtained a most excellent business repute, and has also secured a large and valuable trade connection in Blackburn and the surrounding districts. Mr. Briggs executes all kinds of ordinary printing and bookbinding, and is an account-book manufacturer, besides which he is a general stationer. Special attention is paid to the manufacture of account-books and commercial stationery of all kinds, and a considerable business is done in the binding of periodicals and music, and all kinds of mill-books are ruled to pattern. His premises, at No. 73, Northgate, comprise a spacious warehouse with commodious workshops in the rear, fitted up in good style and equipped in the most complete manner. Printing and bookbinding form the specialities of his trade, and in these departments he is largely patronised. He invariably keeps on hand a first-class stock of stationery goods, and in this branch of the business he is well able to compete with any other house in the same line, whether as regards quality or price. Orders of all descriptions are executed with promptness and dispatch, and work is turned out in the most superior style in every department. A good working staff is constantly employed on the premises, and special orders are undertaken at the shortest notice. Mr. Briggs is a highly-respected tradesman in Blackburn, and he enjoys the confidence and esteem alike of clients and acquaintances.

Dewhurst's Grand Clothing Hall, Higher Church Street, Blackburn.—One of the most attractive establishments, in fact quite an ornament to the town, is that of Mr. J. Dewhurst, popularly known as Dewhurst's Grand Clothing Hall, in Higher Church Street, which is the largest establishment of the kind in East Lancashire, having a very handsome frontage, distinguished by grand pillars and splendid plate-glass windows. However wonderful a sight the exterior of the mart may present, it is nothing to be compared with the large and comprehensive stock in the interior, Mr. Dewhurst being the veritable boys' ideal tailor, and all parents and guardians who wish to see their children or wards economically and fashionably dressed should not fail to pay him a visit. This house is also well known for the production of what is known as Dewhurst's "Fifty Shilling Suit," a really good suit, made of the very best material, in all the latest colours, fashionably cut, and, by reason of its general good appearance, has become one of the leading features of the extensive trade of the establishment. The "Thirty-shilling Suit," too, is also a marvel of what can be produced by an enterprising business man, being made in all the newest materials and finished in the highest style of the tailoring art. The spacious showroom on the first floor is also well filled with ready-made clothing, though this by no means represents the entire trade of the house, as a very extensive high-class bespoke business is carried on with tact, push, and energy, the pervading characteristics of all that is done in the name of Dewhurst. The rapid development of the business has probably been a surprise to many, yet, when it is considered that the cash system is strictly adhered to and the quality of the goods unexcelled, the tremendous sales recorded by the proprietor are only the natural and logical result consequent upon all well organised and honourable commercial operations. There is a branch establishment at Market Street, Darwen, where customers are treated with equal liberality and attention.

J. Shorrock, Wholesale Grocer and Corn Dealer, Lion Tea Warehouse, 1 and 3, Northgate, and 1, Astleygate, Blackburn.—This business was founded nearly a quarter of a century ago by a Mr. John Embley, and was taken over by Mr. Shorrock in 1878. The premises consist of a large double-fronted shop, having a very commanding corner position. Immediately adjoining the main portion of the building there is a single shop used as sale-room and offices, while the chief portion of the establishment forms the wholesale grocery department. The establishment is exceedingly popular and is admirably supported by the trade and under its popular name of the Lion Tea Warehouse is widely known in all parts of the Blackburn district. The extensive stock includes all kinds of general groceries, and among these a very important item is tea, which Mr. Shorrock deals in. He has always a supply of all the finest growths and is particularly noted for his excellent blends. Provisions, sugars, preserves, tinned meats, fish, and many other similar articles also form a large part of the stock. In corn and provender dealing the proprietor has also developed a very extensive business, his premises being well adapted to this class of trade. There is a powerful hoist now worked by one of Crossley's gas engines for lifting the bags and sacks to the various floors, and the whole of the arrangements are decidedly those of a really first-class house. A very extensive trade is done, a large staff is employed, and the business is widely patronised by the trade.

William Wells, Chemist and Druggist, 69, Higher Eanam, Blackburn.—This business was established in the present premises in 1872, by Mr. Wells, who is still the sole proprietor, and who has made his name famous through his discoveries, especially those now so widely known as "Wells' Stomach Mixture" and "Wells' Blood Purifier." Mr. Wells' establishment consists of a handsome front shop with a spacious warehouse in the rear. The shop is most tastefully fitted up and arranged, and it displays a splendid stock of pure drugs, patent medicines and other pharmaceutical preparations; perfumery, fancy soaps, &c. The spacious warehouse in the rear exhibits an immense stock of drysaltery goods as well as agricultural seeds, in which the firm does an extensive trade. The firm's specialities are "Wells' Stomach Mixture," and "Wells' Blood Purifier." With reference to the former of these celebrated preparations, Mr. Wells is in possession of hundreds

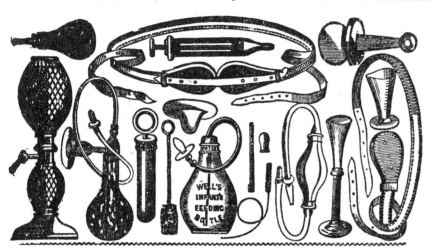

of unsolicited testimonials. No less renowned is Mr. Wells' "Blood Purifier," which when used in accordance with his instructions on each bottle is found to be a perfect cure for old and new sores, ulcerated sores on the neck, blackheads or pimples on the face, scurvy sores, cancerous ulcers, blood and skin diseases, glandular swellings, and clears the blood from all impure matter from whatever cause arising. Both of these valuable preparations are sold in bottles at 1s. and 2s. each, with full directions for use, and they are sent by post to all quarters of the United Kingdom. The trade of this firm is very extensive in all departments. Possessing a high reputation for the excellent quality of everything dealt in and for his scrupulous care in dispensing medicines, Mr. Wells enjoys the confidence of the medical gentlemen of note in and around Blackburn.

Shaw & Porter, Saddlers and Harness Makers, 88, Northgate, Blackburn.—An old and worthy house in the saddle and harness making industry is that of the firm whose name is recorded in the title to this notice, the business having been founded by Mr. Wm. Shaw in 1840, and fifteen years ago the present designation of the firm was assumed on his nephew Mr. John Porter being admitted a partner. The premises occupied comprise a well appointed double-fronted shop with plate glass windows, and in the rear are capacious workshops, where a number of experienced workmen are regularly employed in this branch of industry. Mr. Porter personally superintends the organization of the business. The stock is well worth inspection, consisting of all kinds of harness and saddlery, including van harness, strong cart and trace gears, &c. Excellent specimens are shown in cart collars, saddles and bridles, &c., well made and finished with the very best fittings and workmanship, well suited to withstand the rough wear and tear of cartage work. Superior silver-plated and brass-mounted harness is also shown of lighter construction, combined with equal strength, for carriage work, the quotation for which always commands ready purchasers. Messrs. Shaw & Porter's portmanteaus, bags, hat cases, dress baskets, &c., are known all over the town for their many excellences and high class finish. Messrs. Shaw & Porter have always a nice selection of gentlemen's riding saddles and bridles, driving reins, gloves, whips, leggings, hunting crops, horse clothing, body rollers, bandages, knee caps, bits, spurs, gig aprons and rugs. All kinds of purses, pocket books, dog collars, and leaders. Rug straps, braces, footballs, stable brushes, and combs in stock. Special attention is devoted to ordered goods, everything being done that can be done to promote the prompt and expeditious execution of all orders entrusted to the firm, which has doubtless been a great factor in the immense success that has attended their industrial enterprises. The trade is of a good class and well established. Mr. Porter, who since the death of Mr. Shaw in 1885 has been the sole proprietor of the business, is a gentleman of great enterprise and business ability, and is held in the esteem of all with whom he has business relations.

James W. Page, Mantle and Costume Manufacturer, Station Road, Blackburn.—This business has been in existence about twelve years, and was founded by the present proprietor at the above address, where he occupies spacious and well-appointed premises, admirably adapted to the requirements of the trade and presenting an attractive and elegant appearance. The ground floor, consisting of two large shops, has a very imposing frontage, the first-class display in the windows at once stamping the establishment as one conducted upon the best principles. Devoting his attention entirely to mantles, costumes, and dresses, the proprietor is enabled to guarantee the highest degree of excellence in every detail. The whole of the work is carried out upon the most approved principles, the best of material is used, and only the highest class of workmanship in the manufacture of the various goods is allowed in this establishment. The floors above the showroom are used as workrooms, in which a large number of skilled hands are employed. Not only do the firm keep pace with the most popular fashions of the day but they also make their goods in their own style and design, and have achieved marvellous success in the introduction of attractive novelties. There are few houses in this locality in which could be found such a handsome and valuable stock, or where the firm is so deservedly popular and successful.

British Organette and Organette Music Company, Salford, Blackburn.—Among the various mechanical methods adopted for the production of music in the domestic circle, that exemplified in the organette is probably the best suited for general use, and of these instruments there are few that have gained such an amount of popularity as those constructed by the above company, whose business was originally founded about ten years ago by Mr. J. Draper, who is still the manager, and to his energy, ability, and enterprise the success achieved may be said to be justly due. The works consist of a portion of a large building located in close proximity to the station, and cover a considerable area. The whole of the workshops are admirably equipped with all appliances and plant requisite in the trade, and are complete in every detail. The firm's chief or principal operations may be considered as representing two branches, namely, making the organettes, and also making the organette music. The shape of these instruments, and the *modus operandi* of producing the music are by this time so familiar to every one that it would be superfluous to describe them. The instruments can be made to play anything, practically speaking, because, as the mechanical movements do not depend upon a barrel or cylinder, but upon a length of specially prepared manilla paper perforated upon scientific principles, it is evident that by adding to the length of the paper there is, to all intents and purposes, no limit to the duration of the piece played. Thus, not only will they produce such tunes as hymns, popular airs, reels, polkas, hornpipes, and others of a somewhat limited scope, but they can also be made to play such lengthy pieces as sets of waltzes, quadrilles, &c. The tone of the instruments made by this firm is exceptionally good, and the general construction throughout is highly superior to the majority of instruments of this character. They have, therefore, met with a great demand, not only in the United Kingdom, but also abroad in the various parts of the world. The firm employ a large number of hands making the organettes and the requisite music, both for the home and export trade, and in both these departments command a widespread and extensive business that is still rapidly increasing in all directions.

Mrs. W. Burrow, Baby Linen and Ladies' Under-clothing, &c., Depôt, 72, Wellington Buildings, King William Street, Blackburn.—Mrs. W. Burrow, the proprietress of this fashionable and well-known baby linen and ladies' underclothing establishment, has been in business at the present address since the year 1877, and she has formed a connection in Blackburn and the district which enables her to occupy a leading position in this department of trade. The premises at No. 72, Wellington Buildings embrace a very handsome double shop, with plate-glass windows, and which covers an area of 24 feet by 21 feet. This shop is neatly but elegantly fitted up, and all the appointments are of the most complete character. The stock is large in extent as well as in variety, and the goods comprise everything which is usually to be met with in first-class emporiums of this description; and as regards quality, this establishment possesses a repute second to none in the district, and all orders are carefully and expeditiously executed, and a highly competent staff of assistants are regularly employed on the premises. The business is conducted with tact and ability, and in a manner which has secured for the proprietress a large and influential patronage, and for the house a widespread and enviable popularity.

Alfred P. Garland, Pharmaceutical and Family Chemist, 80, King William Street, Blackburn.—This business, being unique of its kind in the town, calls for special mention in these reviews. It was first founded at 10, Sudell Cross, in 1866, by the present proprietor, Mr. A. P. Garland. Thirty years ago Mr. Garland voluntarily passed all his examinations as a pharmaceutical chemist, then a rare thing, examinations not being at that time compulsory. In 1884 Mr. Garland removed to his present premises, 80, King William Street. His large and handsome shop is carefully arranged in such a way as to make it almost impossible for any of the assistants to make a mistake in dispensing medicines, the poisons being kept in a separate room. Among the preparations by which this house is most popularly known are Garland's Cough Linctus, for the cure of coughs, colds, asthma, bronchitis, consumption, and all affections of the chest, and a celebrated "Tic" mixture, said to be an infallible cure for this distressing complaint. All the novelties in pharmaceutical preparations are taken note of, and as soon as their utility is established they are added to the stock. Prescriptions are dispensed under the careful supervision of the proprietor and the utmost possible care is taken in their preparation. All the drugs and chemicals used in the various processes of manufacture are of the purest and best quality obtainable. He also keeps an immense stock of water filters by the best makers, and almost every description of mineral and aërated waters. In addition to being a pharmacist, Mr. Garland is a very successful dentist, and the display of beautiful artificial teeth almost reconciles the beholder to the loss of his own. Many valuable and useful tooth pastes and powders, mouth washes, &c., are here made and sold at most reasonable prices. He is well known in this district also by professional and amateur photographers, for here may be had every possible requisite which either may require. All the leading kinds of dry plates are kept in stock; mounts of every description; cameras, lenses, back-grounds, and the thousand and one things that go to make up the contents of a photographic studio. Should anything be wanted that is not in stock, the obliging proprietor, who is in constant communication with the best houses, will at once obtain it for his customers. There is also a convenient little dark-room for changing and developing plates, &c., which he places at the disposal of any one requiring it. He also keeps a large stock of scientific apparatus of all kinds, electrical and magnetic batteries, opera glasses, spectacles and eye-glasses to suit all sights, lantern slides, which may be either bought or hired, thermometers, hydrometers, &c., &c. These, with an immense variety of fancy articles, perfumery, soaps of all kinds, and the various novelties usually found in a first-class pharmacy, go to make up a stock the inspection of which must interest and please every one. Mr. Garland has a branch establishment at 24, Foxhall Road, Blackpool. Mr. Garland enjoys the esteem and respect of all those with whom he is associated in business. Quiet and gentlemanly in manner, the well-known high character of his business transactions obtain for him the confidence of all those with whom he comes in contact, and he well deserves the support of his fellow-townsmen.

C. B. Bean, Saddler, &c., Darwen Street, Blackburn.—Prominent among the oldest establishments in Blackburn is the one at 24, Darwen Street, which dates from about 1812, at that time carried on as the saddlery business of Mr. J. Myers, well known throughout the district, and where the late Mr. W. Shaw, saddler, of Northgate, served his apprenticeship. The shop was a short time ago illustrated from a drawing by Mr. Haworth, local artist, and published in the *Blackburn Times*. The shop was next door to Messrs. J. and H. Polding's, one of the oldest cornfactors in the town. Soon after Mr. James Waugh succeeded to the business of Mr. Myers he was obliged to remove from the old shop to larger premises on the opposite side of the way, where he had a large warehouse at the back and good comfortable workshop. Mr. Waugh retired in 1876 and was succeeded by Mr. C. B. Bean, who had acted as his foreman for twelve and a half years. During the time he has been in business he has had the patronage of those who did business with his predecessor. The workshop is next to the Darwen tram office, St. Peter Street; the premises in Darwen Street are now converted into sale and showroom. The shop has a first-class frontage, and the windows present a more than usually attractive appearance, having a handsome life-size model of a horse, which displays harness and saddlery to great advantage. Every description of harness is made and kept in stock, including gig, pair-horse, brougham, and single harness, shandry and cart harness, &c. Saddles are also a great feature and are made upon the latest and most improved styles. The material and workmanship in these goods are both of the very highest order, and the proprietor being himself a thoroughly practical man he is enabled to ensure that superiority of make which has done so much to enhance the credit and reputation of the establishment. Among the chief items of the stock may be mentioned Blackwell's patent dumb jockey, Carter's patent safety shaft tugs, Latchford's patent ladies' safety stirrups, Scott's patent safety stirrups, Barnsby's patent safety stirrup bars, &c.; also all such descriptions of goods as steel bits, &c., riding and driving whips, horse clothing, stable requisites; in addition to which there is a large stock of portmanteaus, Gladstone bags, game bags, rug straps, dog collars, &c. Mr. Bean is also agent for Elliman and Kenyon's Horse Embrocation, and Jem Cooke's celebrated Horse Powders. Mr. Bean commands a very extensive trade in all parts of Blackburn and the surrounding district and has executed a large amount of work for the Corporation, for whom he has successfully completed many important contracts. In his workshops, which are admirably equipped for the production of the best work, he employs an efficient staff of workmen, selected from the most experienced artizans, and conducts the business on a thoroughly sound basis.

J. & W. H. Mellor, Shirtmakers, Hosiers and Glovers, 10, New Market Street, Blackburn.—A house that has recently come prominently into notice in connection with the industry above mentioned is that of Messrs. James and William Higginson Mellor, gentlemen of great experience in this line of business and who founded the house now under review last year. The stock held is large and comprehensive, and of guaranteed quality. A strong part, in fact one of the principal features of the house, is gentlemen's hosiery, a choice variety of which is shown. Mellor's shirts are a well-known speciality throughout the trade; they can be had ready-made and to measure, and being entirely the firm's own make are well abreast of the times for style, fit, and strength. Gloves, too, in all the most reliable makes, are seen in grand display. Driving and hunting gloves and dress gloves in all the leading colours form a great attraction in this well-selected stock, this and all other prominent lines kept on hand by the firm being well worth a visit by intending purchasers. Handkerchiefs in plain, twill and fancy silk, hem-stitched French cambric, with plain and fancy coloured borders, abound in great profusion, and are all decided bargains; collars, cuffs and fronts, in three and four folds linen, best quality, in all the newest and improved shapes. Indeed, this branch of the stock cannot fail to delight all spectators, being far above mediocrity in finish and manufacture and in every respect such as must command extensive sales. Great care has been used in the selection of the goods, and being received from manufacturers of repute they are without exception the best possible value obtainable. The firm also deal in dressing-gowns, rugs, &c., as well as silk umbrellas, summer fancy vests, requisites for evening dress wear, &c.; and every item will bear the strictest scrutiny, and are second to none in quality and value in the market. The trade is extensive, and chiefly confined to the locality. The partners are gentlemen practically acquainted with all the details of the trade carried on, and of the highest commercial status.

Charles Knowles, Commercial and General Printer, Bookbinder, &c., 72, Darwen Street, Blackburn.—This prosperous business was founded by Mr. Knowles at premises in Mill Lane in 1878, and removed to the present address in 1882. The building now occupied comprises a spacious shop and printing-rooms. The shop is well appointed and heavily stocked with a great variety of articles in the stationery line, especially cards. In the rear of the shop is the machine-room, where are treadle printing machines and hand-presses, including one large printing machine by the well-known firm of Harrilds, London. Upstairs on the first floor are the compositors' rooms with a most efficient plant, containing every requisite in type, &c., for the production of all classes of printing in the best possible and economic manner. All kinds of paper is also stored in this part of the edifice, being kept in excellent order and of the best quality. The workmen employed are all picked tradesmen, Mr. Knowles carefully directing the execution of all work entrusted to his care. The great speciality of the house is the printing of business cards, memorial and wedding cards, excellent specimens of which are kept on view. All other kinds of printing are likewise executed with promptness and despatch, while the style is not to be excelled—equal to copperplate in many respects. Bookbinding, too, is also undertaken and turned out of hand in the best possible manner. To each of the various branches of his business the proprietor bestows unremitting attention, with the definite aim to execute every order in such a manner as to give entire satisfaction to those who favour him with their commands. The trade is of a good, steady class, and almost entirely confined to jobbing work for the leading mercantile houses, public institutions, &c., in the town. The proprietor is a practical printer, and a gentleman respected by all with whom he has business transactions.

James and John Lang, Ironfounders, St. Peter's Foundry, Canterbury Street, Blackburn.—This well-known and old-established business was founded about thirty years ago by Mr. Seth Lang in Greaves Street, Blackburn, and conducted by him solely for about twenty years, when he took in partnership his son, James Lang, and the firm traded as Seth Lang & Son. At the death of Mr. Seth Lang in 1883 his son James was left sole proprietor. He entered into partnership with his cousin, Mr. John Lang, who was for many years foreman in the firm of S. Lang & Son, and in November, 1887, he removed to the present large and commodious works, the St. Peter's Foundry, Canterbury Street, which cover an area of about a thousand square yards, and comprise a large moulding shop, fitting and dressing shop, office and large yard. There are two cupolas for melting the iron for the moulding operations, and there is also a useful smithy. The shops are exceedingly well arranged, and fitted with all the necessary mechanical and other appliances, tools, &c. The fitting and dressing shop is very conveniently placed. A very considerable amount of work is done, the castings being chiefly for Blackburn and the surrounding districts. Messrs. Lang have had a lengthy experience as ironfounders, and the work turned out of the St. Peter's Foundry is excellent in material and of first-class workmanship. This firm undertake all kinds of iron casting up to ten tons. Every detail is carried out under the careful personal superintendence of the partners themselves with the greatest care and attention, with the result that nearly every found is a successful one. Messrs. Lang are highly respected by the trading community of the town and district.

George Cross, Wood Turner and Wringing Machine Maker, &c., 36, Clayton Street, Blackburn.—Mr. George Cross commenced business in 1868, in a shop in Furthergate, and to meet the demands of increasing business, removed to larger premises at the Old Barracks in 1870. Finding again the space unequal to his still increasing requirements, he finally removed to his present address in 1886. These premises comprise a large three-storey building, sixty feet by twenty, the ground floor of which is entirely taken up with the necessary power for driving the machinery required by the firm. The first floor is occupied as a saw mill, with circular saws and band saw in constant operation. The upper floor is the large turning shop. Here eight powerful lathes are almost constantly at work. All kinds of material for cabinet work, wringing and washing machine rollers, and repairs of every description for same, are here turned in the most effective manner. A large amount of work is regularly turned out, the trade being principally with the cabinet makers and joiners in Blackburn and the surrounding district, as well as with machine dealers of various kinds. The whole of the work is carried out under the care and personal superintendence of the proprietor, who has now had a large and unique experience in the wood-turning business, in which so many strides of progress have been made during the last quarter of a century. Within Mr. Cross's remembrance the business was carried on by the slow and laborious system of foot power, when the quantity of work turned out was infinitesimally small and at a proportionately large cost of production. Now the largest and the minutest work is all done by the application of steam power, while the quantity of work turned out by modern methods is utterly beyond all comparison with that of the early days of Mr. Cross. It goes without question also that the quality of the new work is immeasurably superior to that produced under foot methods and hand work.

R. J. Duerden, Painter, Gilder, and Decorator, 58, Victoria Street, Blackburn.—Mr. R. J. Duerden commenced business here in 1879, and has a first-class trading connection. The premises comprise a large shop with a handsomely decorated frontage. There is one large plate-glass window, in which a most excellent display of all the very latest designs in paper-hanging goods is made. The shop is well stocked with all kinds of goods pertaining to the business, including a most complete assortment of wall papers of all kinds, from the latest and most expensive design down to the ordinary, but very neat, papers, by which a bare wall may now be so cheaply, yet so comfortably, covered and decorated. There are also dry and moist colours of all kinds; oils, varnishes; and both oil and water-colour paintings of more or less merit, making altogether a stock of considerable variety and value. The basement is occupied as a workshop. Mr. Duerden has a very large and thriving business both in the town and surrounding district, and in an ordinary way he employs about a dozen able and experienced men, which number is of course increased considerably according to the pressure of work. Mr. Duerden himself has had a very extensive and varied experience, and the work completed under his care and superintendence has given the utmost satisfaction to his patrons, both as regards the character of the materials employed and the first workmanship displayed.

George Aspden, Printer, Bookbinder, and Stationer, 40, King Street, Blackburn.—Mr. Aspden commenced business here some twenty-four years ago, in the year 1865, and has established, during that long period, a steady and prosperous trading connection, especially in the "jobbing" trade, and is held in the highest respect and esteem by his fellow-tradesmen and by the trading community in particular. Mr. Aspden's premises consist of a large three-storey building, on the ground floor of which are two excellent printing machines and other presses, the whole of which are driven by a handy little "Otto" gas engine. The first floor is chiefly occupied as the bookbinding, ruling, and general stationery departments, and is a very busy scene of operations. The upper floor is entirely used as storerooms. Mr. Aspden does a very large general business throughout Blackburn and the surrounding district, and he has established an excellent reputation as a printer. He personally superintends the whole of his business, and, with his lengthy and varied experience in every branch of the trade, his customers are enabled to trust him to carry out their orders and commissions in the best and most approved style, as well as with promptitude and care. In conjunction with Mr. Sharples, Mr. Aspden acts as agent for the London and North-Western Railway Company and West Lancashire Railway Company, and during the summer season a most attractive series of excursions are arranged to Blackpool, Southport, Isle of Man, London, and elsewhere. They also arrange for personally conducted and other Continental trips, and represent several important steamship companies, and issue their tickets to all parts of the world.

A scene of intense activity outside Darwen Railway Station.

"Old Aggies", Stepback, near Tockholes, got its name from the lady who lived there and sold intoxicants to travellers. This photo, not previously published, was taken by a Lancaster man a century ago. It shows a board above the door (perhaps the inn-sign), two ladies wearing white aprons (perhaps one was Aggie), some older ladies and some young lads.

Some Darwen chaps out for a walk in Sunnyhurst Woods on a day with no leaves on the trees but mild enough for no top coats.

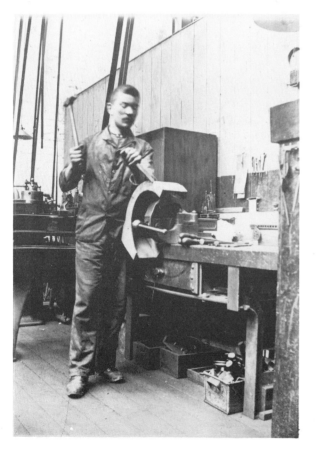

Smell the oil and grime, hear the noises in this engineerin

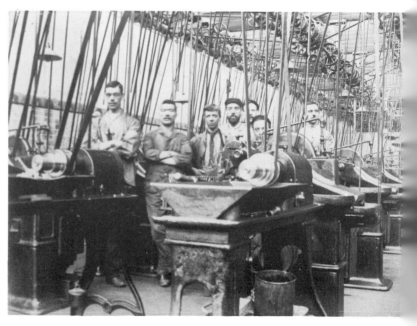

Two female beauties seeking relaxation in Sunnyhurst Wood -
Darwen's safety valve - are caught by a cameraman.

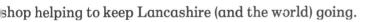

...shop helping to keep Lancashire (and the world) going.

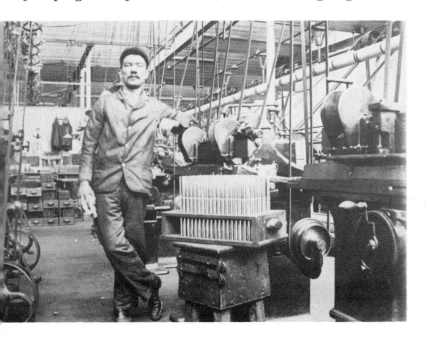

Two postcards that would be easily recognised by the Lancashire folk of a century ago. One shows the clogs worn by most Blegburners and Darreners, with the working man's billy can in which he took a sup of cold tea to work. The other shows the ancestors of todays ragamuffins. It may have been aimed at a mother who had run away from a miserable existence, but was more likely for those who took pleasure in seeing kids playing on t' flags outside their homes.

DARWEN:

ITS GROWTH AND IMPORTANCE.

INDUSTRIES, STATISTICS, AND ILLUSTRATIONS.

 HE historical traditions connected with what is now the busy and populous borough of Darwen are not of a far-reaching or romantic character. There is no doubt that the valley of the Darwen was at one time part of that "forest primeval" which in Saxon times marked this portion of the country, and the noble Roman as well as the primitive Briton may have roamed hither and thither amongst its leafy recesses. As a matter of fact, at the period when "wild in woods the naked savage ran," the ancestors of the men of Darwen, very far removed, may have worshipped Woden on the site where now they worship Trade; they may have launched their coracles on the gleaming waters of the Darwen, and hunted the wild animals of their time and period in the forest on its banks. Roman, Saxon, Dane may have succeeded our ruder forefathers, and have left their mark on places in the vicinity, but in the record of their doings Darwen has no place. It has no historical glories such as pertain to places within easy distance; it is not even accorded the honour of a place in Domesday Book; no wild alarums and excursions of warfare have disturbed its quiet, and no mad convulsions of the State have broken in upon its serenity in the past. Darwen as we know it is in almost every sense a product of the industry of the age. Little more than a century since it was a little cluster of rustic habitations included in the township of Blackburn, having no proper means of communication with the adjacent villages, and showing as little sign of a coming industrial greatness as could well be imagined. True it is that for three or four centuries past coal has been obtained in the district, which is the only portion of old Blackburn parish into which the South Lancashire coal seam extends. Traces of workings which have been exhausted and abandoned are to be seen in many places, whilst "coalers" and "coal-getters" figure among the old-time residents of the village. But if its repute had depended upon its coal, it is to be feared that Darwen would have come sadly off. Independent of the fact that this mineral wealth was not of the highest quality, the seam is nearly worked out, and but little stir is made in the market by its products. Darwen's reputation, as a matter of fact, has been built up upon something more solid than a foundation of coal, and it may be said to date from the time when, towards the end of the last century, the powers that were began to think of improving the roads to and from the then village. With a new road succeeding the badly-made and dangerous paths which connected Darwen with Manchester and other towns, trade began to make its influence felt, and little by little the industry of Darwen commenced to assume a special aspect. The cotton-spinning industry was, of course, that which first began to make headway, and as that has progressed towards the immensity of the present day, so have grown the fortunes of Darwen and its inhabitants. Quite early in the history of this representative Lancashire industry, the favourable position of Darwen led to its being selected for the institution of factories, and in or about 1820 the first mill was erected—a portion of that now known as Bowling Green Mill. This was the commencement of an important era for the men of Darwen, and it is almost incredible to read that a few years later they were so foolish as to join in the outcry against the introduction of machinery into the cotton industry. True, as a part of the parish of Blackburn as then constituted, Darwen can claim a sort of interest in the memory of James Hargreaves, the original inventor of the spinning jenny. A prophet in these days had little honour in his own country, and, as already narrated in our sketch of Bolton, Hargreaves had perforce to leave his native county in consequence of the outcry which was raised against him and his ingenious contrivance. It is curious in these days of ever-multiplying machinery to read of the apparently senseless opposition which was raised to new-fangled ideas in connection with large and important industries. The operatives of a former generation seem to have been of a sadly Tory class—men who were quite content to put up with things as they found them, to be no wiser than their sires, and to take credit unto themselves for their Conservative instincts. The history of the cotton industry supplies many instances of this purblind policy. Many and varied were the experiences of those who endeavoured to show their fellows a means whereby they could revolutionise an industry and make it all their own; opposition and ridicule met them on every hand, and oftener than not ruder and more serious results accrued. The loom-breaking riots which extended over Lancashire in 1826 are a case in point, and it is sad to think of the wanton mischief and grievous loss which those mad-brained proceedings entailed. The adjacent town of Blackburn suffered very severely in this conflict, and not content with doing all they could there, a party of Blackburn boys came over to Darwen and assisted to smash all the looms they could get at, some fifty or sixty which had just been set up by Messrs. Grime, Carr, and others sharing in the general destruction. But these poor and ill-advised men might as well have attempted to sweep back the waters of the mighty Atlantic as to have stemmed

the onward flow of invention in this and other industries, and although the contest was prolonged for a time, prejudice and superstition had at length to give way, and the introduction of machinery became universal. Mills began to rise on every hand in the valley of Darwen, operatives increased and multiplied, they and their employers needed residences and also the necessary commodities of life—hence the village of Darwen began to grow and to spread itself out in all directions. The cotton trade grew and prospered, and concurrently with this increased the industry and progress of Darwen. The splendid mills which are to be seen on all sides attest the spirit of progress which has marked the proceedings of those who have made the town their head centre, and the massive chimney shaft of the Shorrock's factory looks down with pride from an altitude of three hundred feet upon the number of busy hives which are immediately around it. Sixty years is not a long period in the history of a nation, but it has worked wonders in the case of Darwen. It was only in 1820 that Mr. William Eccles opened his first hand-loom establishment at

Bowling Green Mills; and in 1830 Mr. Eccles Shorrock—a relative of the former gentleman—commenced the business which now bears the same family name. Compare the trade of 1830 with that of 1889, and mark the result. Nearly a quarter of a century since, it appears from a return before us, there were in the town of Darwen no less than thirty-six cotton-spinning and weaving mills, with an output valued at two millions and a half sterling annually, and employing nearly eight thousand hands. In 1871, the number of spindles was given at 355,912, and of power looms as 15,136. Since that time a number of new mills have been added, and it may be estimated that at the commencement of the present year there were in Darwen and its precincts something like half a million spindles in constant operation, giving employment to many thousands of men and women.

But the industry of Darwen has not been entirely confined to cotton-spinning. Calico-printing and calico-bleaching have each played a part in the industry of the town. The latter half of the eighteenth century saw several print works in operation at Over

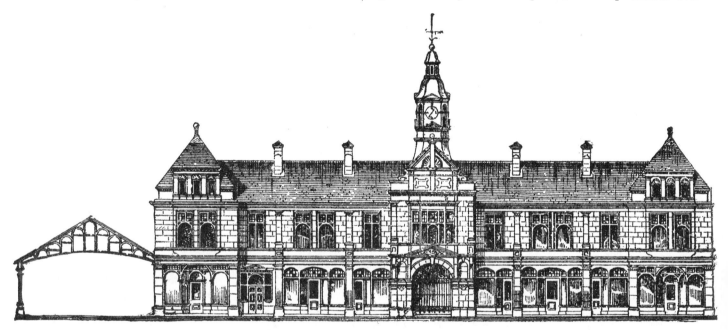

MARKET HOUSE AND MUNICIPAL BUILDINGS, DARWEN.

Darwen, one of the most successful of these being that which was founded by Mr. James Greenway, at Livesey Fold in the year 1776. A very large measure of commercial prosperity seems to have been meted out to this firm, and although there have been several changes in its *personnel* during the course of a hundred and fourteen years, it has still a place in the industry of Blackburn as Heron and Baron's; and with regard to the bleaching industry, it is interesting to note that the Spring Vale Works owe their origin to a man whose name will ever be prominently remembered and honoured in connection with the history of cotton-spinning in Lancashire. It has been related in other pages how Samuel Crompton gave to the nation the benefit of the invention he had made; and when, after much toil and tribulation, he succeeded in obtaining five thousand pounds from a grateful (?) Parliament, he came with his two sons to Darwen and embarked in business there as a cotton-bleacher. In the month of June, 1812, he opened proceedings in what were then known as Hilton's Higher Works, having Low Hill House as his place of residence. So far as can be gathered, the speculation did not prosper—a law-suit regarding the diversion of a spring by mining operations made a hole in the

funds, and from one reason and another, the business had to be suspended in six years from the time of commencement, Mr. Crompton returning to Bolton, where he eventually died, having enriched thousands by his invention, and made next to nothing for himself. Other bleaching works were started in Darwen at or about this time, and some of them survive in a prosperous and busy condition.

Paper-making is another useful branch of industry which has helped to make the name of Darwen famous all over England. The first who engaged in this trade seems to have been a member of the Hilton family, who originally commenced business as bleachers. He it was who, some fifty years since, erected the first paper-mills on the banks of the Darwen. They were reputed at that time to be the best and largest in the United Kingdom, and contemporary records point to the Hilton Mills as employing by far the major portion of the industrial inhabitants. For some years they conducted a very large and wide-spread business, their name becoming well known in all directions; but, in 1843, the concern came to a somewhat inglorious termination. For a time this delayed the progress of the industry in the town; but others soon came forward to take the vacant place, and paper-making is now one of the staple industries of the town, a very large quantity of this valuable commodity being annually turned out. In its way, paper is fully as valuable to the community as cotton, and the quantity of Darwen-made paper is well known and attested in all parts of the kingdom. Iron-casting, earthenware-making, and paper-staining are important features in the work of the townsfolk, and in every direction are to be seen the evidences of a busy and hard-working race.

Referring briefly to the chief events in the local history, it may be noted that the Act for a railway between Bolton, Darwen, and Blackburn was passed in 1845, and this was the commencement of a series of iron ways which now connect the town by means of the Lancashire and Yorkshire Railway and its allies with every portion of the kingdom. Gas, another important auxiliary to progress, was provided in 1840, at which date gas-works were erected at a cost of £8,000. The Local Board was formed in 1854, and for a period extending over a quarter of a century its members administered the affairs of the township with a manifest care for its progress and comfort. At that time the population was just over eleven thousand, and when, in 1877, this had more than doubled, it was felt that the time had arrived when Darwen should take upon itself the heavy responsibility of a mayor and corporation. The ratepayers were accordingly bidden to a meeting in the Co-operative Hall, and on the 20th March, 1877, they passed a resolution in favour of Incorporation. A few months later a Government inspector came down to see whether there was any just cause or impediment, and in the November following the gratifying intelligence was conveyed to the town that the Lords

of the Privy Council had been graciously pleased to grant a charter of incorporation. It was on the 25th of March in the following year that the all-important document arrived in the town; and a red-letter day that would seem to have been in the history of Darwen. Mr. Snape, chairman of the Local Board, was the bearer of the parchment, and on his arrival at the station from Manchester, he was met by an enthusiastic crowd and escorted in triumph to the Local Board offices, the bells of Holy Trinity ringing out a merry peal meanwhile. The first Town Council was elected on the 1st of July, 1878, and Mr. Snape was appropriately elected to the high office of Mayor, which he held for three successive years.

The same year which witnessed the incorporation of the borough was notable also for some serious disturbances in connection with the weavers' strike. On May-day some two or three thousand weavers had met on the Fair Ground and agreed to a levy on those in work for the benefit of the strikers. A few days later the riot commenced at the Top o' th' Hagg by the burning of an effigy of Richard Sharples. Window-smashing and other destructive amusements became general, and it was not until the next day that an increased body of police were able to cope with the rioters and to provide some of the leaders with free lodging. A time of excitement ensued which was common to Lancashire, the troops having to be called out in Blackburn and other towns, but eventually the difficulties were settled, and matters resumed their normal condition. Since that time, the history of Darwen has been of a comparatively unexciting character. Nothing but steady progress has been noted on all hands. Industry has grown and prospered. The workers and those who employ them have been on the best of terms; the comfort and convenience and health of the residents have been well cared for by the authorities; and in every respect Darwen has maintained its reputation as a typical Lancashire town.

PROPOSED NEW TOWN HALL, DARWEN.

THE CHURCHES, &c.

The church of St. James, which is situate on a hill in the eastern suburb of the town, is of the oldest foundation, and a direct successor to the "Darwent Chappell," with which at one time the residents had to be content. It is conjectured that this chapel had its origin in the time of Good Queen Bess, previous to which there seems to have been no provision whatever for the

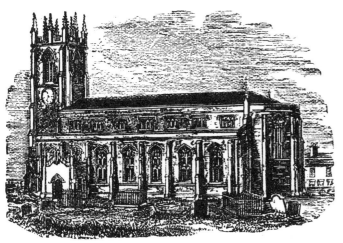

HOLY TRINITY CHURCH, DARWEN.

spiritual wants of Darweners, who had to be satisfied with the crumbs which fell from the mother church at Blackburn. The Presbytery of 1646 seems to have appointed Mr. Joshua Bernard minister at Darwen, and have made him "passing rich at forty pounds a year." After the Restoration once a month was thought sufficient service for Darwen, a curate coming over from Blackburn for the purpose, and a nice little dispute was occasioned by some sturdy Nonconformists being of opinion that they might as well use the building. The chapel was rebuilt about 1698, and so it remained until the middle of the present century, when it was substantially restored and reopened in 1853. The style is somewhat mixed, Gothic-porched arches mingling with architecture of a later period, and there is nothing remarkable about the interior. The church of Holy Trinity dates from the year 1829, when it was erected by means of a Parliamentary grant at a cost of £6,799. This is a capacious building in the florid Gothic style, and contains about one thousand three hundred sittings. There is a handsome tower at the west end in which is placed a peal of half a dozen bells, the sound of which, floating across the quiet town, is a pleasant feature of Sunday in Darwen. St. Paul's, Hoddesdon, St. John's, Turncroft, and St. Cuthbert's are district churches, all of them being built in the Gothic style of architecture, the edifice of St. John's being a very chaste specimen of that style, and costing £11,500.

The Nonconformists have always been a busy body in this vicinity, and in times of persecution, as well as in those of toleration, they have kept the light of faith alight. Many secluded portions of the moors have seen their gatherings, and Mr. Sagar, whose name is held in respect by all Nonconformists, was one of their most zealous leaders in the seventeenth century, imprisonment in Lancaster Gaol not even closing his mouth. In 1687 Mr. Charles Sagar became the first stated minister of the "Meeting" at Over Darwen, and from the passing of the Act of Toleration in the succeeding year the Nonconformist body seems to have grown in strength and importance until its members form no inconsiderable portion of the community, and possess a number of handsome and commodious places of worship which space will not allow us to enumerate.

THE PUBLIC BUILDINGS

of Darwen are not at the present moment very numerous in character, but there are not wanting signs and indications of several additions thereto. The Market House and Municipal Buildings, of which we give an illustration, constitute a handsome block, having a clock tower in the centre, and well equipped for the transaction of business in both departments. These, however, have proved insufficient for the wants of Darweners, and on the preceding page we give a view of the New Town Hall which will shortly be available for the use of the inhabitants. This will be a noble building having a handsome tower over the central entrance, and a spacious hall for public meetings, &c. Accommodation will also be found for the principal officials of the Corporation, and in every respect the New Town Hall promises to be a worthy addition to the local institutions of Darwen.

THE PRESS.

The Fourth Estate is represented in Darwen by the *Darwen News*, which was established in the year 1874 as a Liberal organ. Mr. J. J. Riley, of Market Street, is the present proprietor, and in his hands it has made most steady and satisfactory progress, its well-printed pages, eight in number, containing a complete *resumé* of the local history of the week, as well as capital comments thereon. A yearly Handbook of Local History, published by Mr. Riley, is also much appreciated. The Conservative party is represented by the *Darwen Post*, which was established so recently as 1885. It is published by Mr. R. Timperley at Bank Top Works, and is a very well-edited and got-up journal.

PARLIAMENTARY REPRESENTATION.

Prior to the passing of the Redistribution Act of 1885 Over and Lower Darwen were included in the North-Eastern Division of

ST. JOHN'S CHURCH, DARWEN.

Lancashire, formed by the Act of 1868. They now, however, give a name to the new Darwen Division of the county, in which, under the extended franchise, there are nearly thirteen thousand voters. The last election took place in 1886 and resulted in the return of Viscount Cranborne (son of Lord Salisbury), by a majority of 730 over Mr. John Slagg (Gladstonian Liberal).

DARWEN.

J. & W. Tomlinson, Colliery Agents, Darwen.

—The business carried on by the well-known firm of Messrs. J. & W. Tomlinson is one that is of the greatest importance in a large manufacturing district like that of Darwen, and is therefore deserving of special mention in these pages. It was founded considerably over twenty years ago, and has made very rapid progress, until at the present time the firm are probably the largest dealers in coal, cannel, furnace and gas coke, to be met with in Lancashire. This is saying a great deal for the extent of their operations, for owing to the great number of works of all kinds to be found in such profusion throughout the County Palatinate, there is daily an enormous consumption of every description of fuel. Their chief office is at Darwen, but they also have offices at Wardleworth for Rochdale and south-east Lancashire, at Burnley for a district extending from Sowerby-Bridge to Skipton, at Blackburn for north Lancashire, also at Bolton and Horwich for the district contiguous thereto. In addition to acting as merchants, Messrs. J. & W. Tomlinson have the sole sale of the coal raised at several of the largest Lancashire and Yorkshire collieries. It is probably to this fact that the extensive trade of Messrs. Tomlinson is largely due, the operations of the firm extending over north, east, and south Lancashire, together with a regular trade with North Wales and intermittent business with Barrow in the North and London in the South. The firm not only supply fuel of every description to private buyers, but also a large number of merchants and dealers in coal. The business is conducted with great energy and ability, and occupies a leading position in the mercantile industry of Lancashire.

J. Place & Sons, Hoddlesden Fireclay Works, Darwen.

—The well-known firm of Messrs. Joseph Place & Sons, of the Hoddlesden Collieries and Fireclay Works, near Darwen, both from an industrial and commercial point of view, is undoubtedly one of the largest and most influential in this district, and has had trade relations with Darwen and Hoddlesden for more than fifty years. Half a century ago two brothers, Messrs. John and Joseph Place, were extensively engaged in the spinning and weaving industry here. They built at a later date the fine weaving-shed now in the occupation of Alexander Carus, Esq., J.P., and known as the St. Paul's Mill. The Place family has been connected with the colliery industry for upwards of fifty years. In 1863, Mr. Joseph Place, the younger brother, withdrew from the cotton manufacture, leaving his brother in possession of the three mills, he taking the colliery branches of the business. At the outset nothing but coal was sought for, but a splendid bed of fireclay having been discovered, it entered into the mind of the proprietor to establish a new and most extensive business than had hitherto been carried on in connection with the coal trade, viz., the manufacture of fire-clay and sanitary goods. The opening of the branch line in 1876 from the Blackburn and Manchester Railway of the Lancashire and Yorkshire Company greatly facilitated the development of this business. This valuable bed of fireclay, which is well known in the district as the "Lower mountain mine fireclay," is admirably adapted to the manufacture of all kinds of sanitary ware as pipes, elbows, joints, traps, gullies, fire-bricks, chimney-pots; these are made in every variety of shape and in pleasing and artistic designs, blocks for boiler seatings, perforated grates, pig and cattle troughs, cisterns, floor-tiles and flue-covers, garden edge-tiles, flower-pots and rustic work, &c. Some idea of the magnitude of the operations carried on in this industry by Messrs. J. Place & Sons may be gathered from the fact that last year two hundred miles of straight sanitary pipes of all dimensions, together with a proportionate amount of fittings, as junctions, bends, traps, &c., were manufactured and sent out from the Hoddlesden Fireclay Works. The machinery and appliances throughout the works are of the most modern description, and embody all the latest improvements and most comprehensive utilities. Amongst other noticeable features may be mentioned a continuous chain for conveying or hauling trucks filled with coal, &c., to the loading depots, 2,000 feet of this chain working on the surface, and 10,000 feet below ground. Messrs. Joseph Place & Sons have practically created this village: they found it a few straggling cottages, but by developing the various industries associated with their name, it has become quite a prosperous and thriving neighbourhood. The trade controlled by this firm is of a widespread, influential, and steadily growing character. Mr. Joseph Place, the founder of the business, died in 1881, very deeply regretted. The surviving partners are Mr. John Edwin and Mr. William Henry Place. Both these gentlemen take an active part in the business, which is conducted throughout with that spirited enterprise and well-directed energy which has always so strongly animated the members of this firm

J. J. Riley, "News" Office, Darwen.

—This business, which was established eighteen years ago by Mr. Riley with one boy as his assistant, is now the foremost of the kind in Darwen. The premises in Market Street consist of a handsome front shop, which is tastefully fitted up, and it displays to advantage a valuable stock of office stationery. There are also many splendid specimens of bookbinding, ruling, and printing in ledgers, day-books, cash-books, journals, wage-books, &c. The works, in William Street Yard, were opened in 1885, the event being celebrated by a banquet, at which Mr. Riley met a hundred and twenty of the leading inhabitants of Darwen and the surrounding districts. They are of large extent, measuring 110 feet long by 50 wide, and consist of a handsome building of two storeys in height, used as reporters' rooms and offices, with spacious printing establishment in the rear, and equipped with machinery of most approved character. These works are acknowledged by several trade journals to be the most perfect in the district, and have been designated "model printing offices" by the highest authorities. The *Darwen News*, through which this house is probably most widely known, since it became the property of Mr. Riley has quadrupled its circulation and has been increased in size. As an advertising medium, this admirable publication is greatly taken advantage of by tradesmen belonging to all industries in and around Darwen; and its racy articles, interesting local notes, and useful information on all subjects makes it much appreciated by all classes of the people. In the letterpress department a large business is done in these works, Mr. Riley having secured the Darwen Corporation contracts for ten years in succession. The excellence of the workmanship and artistic taste that characterise the products of all departments, the energy and honourable methods through which this business was formed, maintain a demand which keeps the works and thirty hands constantly employed, the business connection being very extensive and of the most influential order. Mr. Riley is a well-known gentleman, and his frank, courteous manner and high personal qualities have won for him the respect of his numerous warm supporters and all with whom he meets. He is one of the most active members of the Blackburn Board of Guardians, and has a seat upon all the important committees. He is also, and has been for years, one of the Free Library Commissioners. For several years he has been connected with the successful limited company known as the Darwen Manufacturing Company as a director. In 1885 Mr. Riley purchased a newspaper in the Rossendale Valley, which he has continued to run most successfully. The *Rossendale Free Press* to-day is the leading newspaper in Rossendale, and already employs the largest staff in the valley. The *Free Press*, with its jobbing department, finds constant employment for nearly twenty hands.

Harwood Bros., New Bridge Mill, Darwen.

—This time-honoured mill was built in 1848 by Mr. Thomas Howarth, of the firm of Howarth, Walsh & Ainsworth, and up to about 1860 was worked by this firm. Mr. Thomas Gillibrand held the concern until 1868, when he was succeeded by Messrs. T. and J. Eccles. In 1875 Messrs. Harwood and Eccles assumed the reins, and until March, 1888, they continued to work the mill in partnership, trading as Messrs. Harwood & Eccles. A dissolution then took place, the brothers Harwood retaining the New Bridge Mill and Mr. Eccles taking the Two Gates Mill. The premises at the New Bridge Mill comprise a large two-storey building, in which the preliminary processes are conducted, also a fine and well-proportioned weaving shed, together with extensive warehouse accommodation, engine and boiler houses, a suite of well-appointed offices and counting-house, and all the accessories of a thoroughly organised establishment. The machinery and appliances are of the most modern construction, and embody all the latest improvements and the most comprehensive utilities, besides an adequate amount of winding, warping, and sizing machinery. The weaving shed contains 387 looms made by J. and R. Shorrock, of Darwen. Of the two engines, one is a "beam;" the other is a horizontal. The boiler is of the Lancashire type, made by Anderton, of Church Accrington, and furnished with all the latest improvements. Messrs. Harwood Bros. give employment to upwards of 180 workpeople, and manufacture chiefly grey cloth, shirtings, &c. These goods are in great demand both for the home and foreign markets, and have an unsurpassed reputation for superior and uniform quality, and excellence of finish. Messrs. Harwood Bros. have a first-class business connection, which is well founded upon the eminent reputation so long enjoyed and the high commercial standing of the firm. The business in every department receives the strict personal attention of the proprietors, and is conducted throughout with marked ability, energy, and enterprise. Messrs. Harwood Bros. have been long and honourably connected with Darwen and the advancement of the best interests of the town and district.

J. W. Butterfield (late Hornby), **Chemist, &c.,** 33, Market Street, Darwen.—This well-known pharmaceutical establishment was founded by Mr. R. W. Hornby at this address in 1881, in whose name it was conducted until 1888, when Mr. J. W. Butterfield was admitted a partner. At the commencement of 1889 Mr. Butterfield became sole proprietor. The pharmacy is centrally situated, has a fine street frontage, and a well-appointed interior. The stock, too, is large and comprehensive, and of the best and finest quality, all the purest and best drugs, chemicals, and pharmaceutical preparations being kept on hand, together with pomades, perfumes, soaps, and toilet requisites of every description, as well as patent medicines and proprietary articles of established repute. Also a large and varied selection of surgical appliances, viz., trusses, belts, elastic stockings, knee caps, enemas, &c. The principal, being a gentleman of great experience in some of the best businesses in London, Liverpool and Birmingham in this scientific vocation, realises the great responsibility of those who dispense medicines, and accordingly bestows special attention to that particular branch of his business; and all physicians' prescriptions, family and private recipes entrusted to his care are promptly and accurately dispensed with drugs and chemicals of guaranteed strength and purity, as directed by the Royal College of Physicians, &c. Orders by post for this department are executed with the utmost dispatch. Conspicuous among the many specialities for which the house has a high reputation is medicinal cod-liver oil, which has now been in increasing demand for some time, which, more than all that can be said and done, testifies to its immense appreciation by the public generally. It is prepared by a special process which renders it almost tasteless and odourless, yet retains all its medicinal virtues. One marked superiority this oil has over that commonly sold is that it is easily digested by the weakest stomach and no nauseous eructations follow its use. His Antiseptic Tooth-powder and Mouth Wash are likewise renowned all over the neighbourhood for their many excellences, imparting as they do a delightful fragrance to the breath and pearly whiteness to the teeth, and when regularly used undoubtedly prevent toothache and decay. A qualified dental surgeon is in attendance for fitting artificial teeth, &c., &c. Another speciality for which they are celebrated is their harmless and painless process for extracting teeth without gas, which it is scarcely necessary to say is very extensively patronised by the public and highly eulogised by the press. He is also sole agent in Darwen and district for Mr. Henry Laurance, the famous London optician. The *clientèle* of the house is of a first-class character, extensive and well-established among the principal families of the town and suburbs. Mr. Butterfield is a gentleman of the highest eminence in his profession, and his qualification as an associate of the Pharmaceutical Society ranks among the highest attainable.

The Darwen Paper Mill Company, Limited, Spring Vale Paper Mill, Darwen.—This company originated under the auspices of the leaders of the co-operative movement in Darwen about eighteen years ago, the site at Lower Darwen (now occupied by the company's brown paper mill) being chosen. A "brown" mill was erected there in 1871, and has proved a distinct success in its working. Encouraged by this signal prosperity of their first venture, the company acquired the Spring Vale site for the erection of a white paper mill in 1873. The work was pushed forward rapidly; the mill was completed in 1874, and very soon three paper-making machines of the best type were in busy operation. These have since been greatly improved, and all the resources of the mill have been advanced to the highest level of productive efficiency. The works and plant now existent are of the most substantial character, and have cost about £90,000. The mill covers a ground area of over 12,000 square yards, and is admirably situated near the head waters of the river Darwen, from which, and from underground sources, a good supply of water is always available. The Spring Vale Mill produces 120 tons of news printing paper every week. This is sent out in webs or reels as required for the modern printing-press, each web containing near four miles of paper. In this way the mill turns out every twenty-four hours more than two hundred lineal miles of news printing paper. The Lower Darwen Mill—the scene of the company's first industrial efforts—is situate about three miles lower down the Darwen than Spring Vale, and produces weekly about eighty tons of brown and grocers' wrapping-papers. The Company employ about 400 hands, and, enjoying an eminent reputation for the sound quality of their manufactures, they control a very large, widespread, and reliable trade. For sixteen years the affairs of the concern have been directed solely by the class of men who originated it, free from any outside patronage or aid, and with but one object—the promotion of the company's welfare; and admirably have their managerial exertions succeeded. The whole of the share capital has long ago been paid back to the shareholders in profits, and the mills are equipped and ready for any competition in the trade they exemplify. For rectitude in their dealings and energy and enterprise in the conduct of their business, the Darwen Paper Mill Company, Limited, are favourably known throughout that branch of industry and commerce in which they are concerned; and the prosperity of the organization and the high repute it enjoys are the best tributes possible to the active ability and honourable efforts of those to whom credit is due for its inception, establishment, and subsequent effectual administration.

Alexander Carus, St. Paul's Mill, Hoddlesden, near Darwen.—The extensive business now carried on by Mr. Alexander Carus, at the St. Paul's Mill, Hoddlesden, was originally established by Mr. John Place, who, in partnership with his brother, built the mill in 1867. These gentlemen were succeeded by Messrs. J. & R. Knowles from whom the business passed into the hands of Mr. Alexander Carus, the present proprietor, in 1882, who has carried on the business with conspicuous success. The premises are very extensive and commodious. The main building is a handsome stone structure of three storeys; there is also extensive warehouse accommodation, engine and boiler house, a spacious suite of well-appointed offices and counting-house, and all the accessories of a large and thoroughly organised establishment. The weaving shed is remarkable, owing to its extra height, allowing to the workers very ample breathing space. The machinery, which is all new, and appliances, are of the most modern description, and embody all the latest improvements and most comprehensive utilities. In addition to a large amount of preparatory and supplementary machinery, the firm run six hundred looms, made chiefly by Messrs. J. and R. Shorrock, of Darwen, and other eminent specialists in weaving machinery. Four hundred and fifty of these looms are "dobbies" for weaving fancy goods, and fifty are what are technically called Jacquard looms. The motive-power is communicated from two horizontal engines made by Richard Walker & Brothers, Bury, of a combined force of 240 h.-p. The firm give regular employment to upwards of three hundred work-people, and keep in constant use several horses and carts engaged in the delivery of their own goods to the railway station in the village. Passenger traffic has not yet been opened out, but is expected in a short time. The establishment of railway communication for goods has given a great impetus to the industry of the district. The class of goods manufactured at St. Paul's Mill are principally plain and fancy dhootees cambrics, Turkey reds, and fine jaconets, twills, sateens, damasks, and brocades. These goods have an unsurpassed reputation in the market for superior and uniform quality, improved design, and excellence of finish, which is justly attributable to the great care and sound judgment exercised in the various processes of fabrication, under the personal supervision of the proprietor, and the splendid machinery the firm have at their command. The business connections are of a widespread, influential, and steadily growing character, and in addition to the extensive home trade, the goods of this firm are largely exported to the Continent, America, and the colonies. Mr. Alexander Carus, who is the sole proprietor, is a Justice of the Peace for Darwen, and occupying as he does such a prominent and influential position in social and mercantile circles, Mr. Carus is well known and highly esteemed for his active exertions in promoting the best interests of the commerce and manufactures of Darwen and the district, and the physical and moral welfare of the industrial community. As an evidence of the interest he takes in his work-people, Mr. Carus has recently completed the erection of fourteen houses for the better domestic accommodation of a portion of his employés. Mr. Carus also takes great interest in technical education, and is on the committee of management of the local technical school.

The Bolton Road Spinning Company, Darwen Mills, Darwen.—Prominent among the many large establishments which contribute so materially to the industrial and commercial prosperity of this busy district are the extensive works of the Bolton Road Spinning Company, so well and widely known as the Darwen Mills. This is one of those splendid mills built by Messrs. Eccles, Sharrock & Co., of Darwen, once the proprietors of no less than six large cotton mills in this town, including the celebrated "India" Mill. The Darwen Mill was built in 1850, entirely of stone construction. The main building is three storeys high, and only separated from its sister establishment, the "India" Mill, by the extensive paper mill of Messrs. Dimmock & Co. The Darwen Mill is exclusively devoted to cotton spinning, and is equipped throughout with a splendid plant of machinery and appliances, embodying all the latest improvements, and including, in addition to the necessary amount of preparation machinery, 50,000 spindles, made by the celebrated firm of Messrs. Platt Bros., of Oldham. The arrangements throughout are admirable, and well exhibit that great care and attention bestowed by the management, not only on the economy of working, but also for the safety, health, and comfort of the numerous employés. The two beam engines are splendid specimens of the work of Messrs. W. & J. Yates, of Blackburn, and of a combined force of 720 indicated horse-power. The three Lancashire boilers, each 30 by 7, are by Messrs. D. Adamson & Co., Dukinfield, near Manchester, and furnished with all the latest improvements. The yarn manufactured is chiefly weft and twist, and has an unsurpassed reputation in the market for strength, consistency, and uniform quality, justly attributable to the great care and sound judgment exercised in the selection and management of the raw material and the splendid machinery the company have at their command. Upwards of two hundred hands are regularly employed. The manufacture in every department is under direct and careful supervision, and is conducted throughout with marked ability, energy, and enterprise. The company have a first-class business connection, which is well founded upon the eminent reputation so long enjoyed and the thorough confidence established by the well-known character and uniform quality of their productions.

Thos. Gillibrand & Sons, Manufacturers, Hollin Grove Mill, Darwen.—This mill, which was built in 1868 by the senior partner of the firm and was founded in 1838, consists of three floors, has a frontage of over 300 feet, and covers a very large area. There are no less than 1,300 looms of the most improved and modern construction, the motive power being provided by a very powerful engine of the latest type. In addition to the usual weaving sheds there are such rooms as the winding-rooms, tape-room, drawing-room; also a mechanics' shop fitted with engine and lathe, in which all important repairs are executed. The firm are noted for the production of various fabrics which are technically known by titles some of which are more familiar to the trade than with the general public. One of the leading features is that of brocades, and among others are brilliantes, coloured and plain crimps, coloured and plain bordered handkerchie's, brocade handkerchiefs, fancy stripes and checks, matalasses, mulls, jaconets, cambrics, and shirtings. In all these the scale of production is enormous, and the firm turn out an immense quantity of goods. Most of these are intended for export purposes, the greater proportion being sent to the Eastern markets, China, India, &c. In all these parts the name of the firm is well known in the trade, and their goods meet with a very ready sale. The whole of the business is conducted upon thoroughly sound commercial principles, and it is only necessary to briefly refer to the influential position held by the proprietors in order to emphasise that fact. R. T. Gillibrand, Esq., and J. W. Gillibrand, Esq., are both magistrates for the borough of Darwen, and the latter gentleman is also a member of the Darwen Town Council. They are both widely known and respected and fill an important position in the mercantile world.

Messrs. Graham Fish & Co., Cotton Manufacturers, Woodside Mill, Darwen.—This business was established in 1851 by Mr. Doctor Graham, Mr. Henry Green, Mr. Thomas Fish, and Mr. John Kay, who successively retired, and in 1880 the firm assumed the present title. The premises are very extensive and commodious. The main building is a large stone structure, three storeys high, of solid and substantial appearance, admirably arranged. The works also contain a large stone building of two storeys, having a frontage of 120 feet and used as a cloth warehouse and yarn store, together with engine and boiler houses and all the accessories of a large and thoroughly organised establishment; the large weaving shed contains 945 looms by the most noted makers, and on the upper floors are two sizing and three winding and warping rooms, replete with machinery and appliances of the most improved description. The motive power is derived from two very fine engines, one horizontal and one vertical, made by Yates. The two boilers are by Yates, of Blackburn, and Hill & Sons, Heywood, and are furnished with appliances for consuming the smoke. The firm manufacture goods suitable for the Eastern markets, dhooties being a leading speciality. These goods have an unsurpassed reputation in the trade for superior and uniform quality and excellence of finish. In Manchester Messrs. Graham Fish & Co. have a warehouse and office at No. 30, Pall Mall, where they hold a large and comprehensive stock, replete with all the best features of this branch of the cotton manufacturing industry. The business in every department is under direct and careful supervision, and is conducted throughout with marked ability, energy and enterprise, upwards of 450 hands being regularly employed. The works at all times present a busy and animated scene of industrial activity. The trade is almost exclusively export, Egypt, India, China and Japan being the principal markets. One of the partners, Graham Fish, Esq., is a justice of the peace for the borough of Darwen, a member of the County Council, and is highly esteemed for his active exertions in promoting the best interests of the commerce and industries of the town and district.

Henry Yates & Sons, Cotton Waste and Paper Stock Merchants, &c., Darwen, Lancashire.—This extensive business was established in 1873, and is now recognized as one of the largest and most influential houses in the trade. The offices and warehouse of the firm are situated at Nos. 47 to 53, Railway Road, and occupy almost an entire block of buildings. They are most conveniently located with reference to the railway, being within less than a hundred yards of the Darwen station of the Lancashire and Yorkshire Railway Company. Besides the very large business done as waste merchants, Messrs. Henry Yates & Sons are also manufacturers of blowings, export flys, and cotton flocks. The works, known as the Nancy Street Mill, are well adapted to the business, and fitted up with all the necessary machinery and appliances for carrying on a large trade. Within the past twelve months the firm has established another mill, known as the Sydney Factory, Moor Lane, Preston. This is now in full work. The works present a busy and animated scene of industrial activity. The business in every department and at all the works is under direct and careful supervision and is conducted throughout with marked ability, energy, and enterprise. Messrs. Henry Yates & Sons have a first-class business connection, and control a trade which is of a widespread, influential, and steadily increasing character. The firm occupies a prominent and influential position in mercantile circles, and both in the extent of their industrial operations and the importance of their commercial transactions Messrs. Henry Yates & Sons rank with the largest firms in this line in Lancashire, and are recognised in a wide sphere as energetic and enterprising men, with whom it is pleasant and profitable to have business transactions.

James Pilkington, Contractor, Sunny Bank Saw Mills, Darwen.—This business was founded twenty-eight years ago by Mr. James Pilkington, and now enjoys a position in the front ranks. The premises are of large extent, and consist of saw mills, joinery works, offices, spacious timber yard, &c. The latter contains an immense stock of rough, sawn, and seasoned woods, including pitch and other pines, spruce, English and foreign oak, &c. Entered by a large gateway, where there is a large weighing machine and handsome suite of offices, the works are equipped in first-class style with all the most approved machinery. The trade of the firm is very extensive, there being always from one hundred to one hundred and fifty hands employed. Among the more important contracts executed by this firm are included the building of the Darwen Spinning Company's Mill complete, the joinery work of Albert Spinning Mills, building the Starkie Street Primrose Mill, March House Lane Mill, the joinery work for Cotton Hall Mills, the building complete of St. John's Schools and Culvert Schools. In addition to these, this firm executed the joinery work for the Catholic chapel, and built the Spring Vale Paper Mills, Hampden Mills, St. John's Vicarage, and numerous other well-known structures in and around Darwen. The practical experience in all departments, the energy, and the honourable methods through which this business was formed continues to maintain and extend the old-established reputation of the firm. Mr. Pilkington is a well-known gentleman, and his frank, agreeable manner and upright principles have gained for him the respect of all with whom he meets, whether in connection with business or matters affecting the public interests.

The Collins Paper Mill Company, Limited, Collins Mill, Darwen.—This is one of the chief houses in the trade, being well known for its specialities, such as medicated felt for the underpacking of carpets, matting, rugs, &c. It is well noted for its manufacture of "The Camphorated Patent Sponge Carpet Lining" (Patent 2,485, registered trade mark, sponge, No. 58,746). This new carpet lining is now to be had from all the leading carpet houses, and is made 1½ yards wide, with a fine canvas back and requires no making as the edges are cut to gauge and lay perfectly flat and straight. This canvas is placed on the back of the pulp whilst the lining is being manufactured, and camphor is also introduced whilst the pulp is in a wet state, and so intermixed that it will prevent moth or insect, as is the case with felt carpet lining. It is warm and noiseless, and can be laid under oilcloth or linoleum to very great advantage. The mill is well known, and has long had a first-class connection amongst the shippers and users of brown and rope paper, and at present it is the only brown mill in Darwen.

Greenwood's Trimming Shop, 209, Duckworth Street, Darwen.—A house that has rapidly risen in public estimation and esteem is that of Mr. Greenwood, who founded the business at the above address last year, 1888, but nevertheless the house has a high reputation all over Darwen for the superior quality of its productions. The euphonious title ascribed to the establishment is due to the fact that the proprietor has made trimmings of all kinds one of his great specialities, which is further evidenced by the enormous stock kept on hand in this particular line. Ladies will do well to inspect the same as there are several novelties not seen every day. He also does a large business in ribbons, laces, and fancy drapery, all of which appears in grand display, and are warranted the best workmanship and material. Another speciality is the ladies' glove department. The stock of kid and silk gloves on hand is very extensive and well assorted, the most reliable makes only being kept, while dress gloves are to be obtained in all the leading colours and sizes. Plain and fancy hosiery, too, in wool, silks, cashmere, merino, &c., in all the Scotch and other best makes, also constitutes a strong part of the stock, and includes handkerchiefs, ladies' collars, cuffs, three and four folds, best quality, in all the newest and improved shapes, scarves and ties, in satin, silk, cambric, and cashmere, especial care having been taken to select the latest novelties. A word will not be out of place about the corsets, which are a speciality here. There are some admirably adapted for young persons, in which cords are substituted for bones and steels, and made to fasten with either a laced back and button front, or clasp front and laced back. Shoulder-straps, whereby the weight of the skirts are removed from the hips, are another distinctive feature about some of the corsets on view here, which look very conducive both to health and comfort. Another focus of attraction is a beautifully made corset without any distinguishing name, which, instead of being cut all in one piece, is fitted with gores, which add materially to the comfort of the wearer and imparts a very trim and *svelte* appearance so much admired in society circles and elsewhere. Although there are numerous specialities that demand notice patrons will please remember that every possible requisite in the fancy drapery and hosiery line are kept in stock at this establishment, the proprietor taking good care to keep well abreast of the times by supplying his customers with everything they require in the particular line of commerce represented by his house. There are some umbrellas, however, in silk lavantine, and the new warranted covers, on paragon frames, with well-selected handles, &c., which alone are well worth a visit. The trade, though only so recently established, is very satisfactory and steadily increasing. Mr. Greenwood is a practical tradesman and a gentleman of the highest commercial status.

Joseph Westwell, Joiner, Builder, &c., Cavendish Street Saw Mills, Darwen.—This business was established in 1883 by the present proprietor, and carried on with great success in the old works up to the beginning of 1888, when a disastrous fire occurred, causing a slight suspension of the operations, which however were resumed with increased vigour in the spring of the year in a large and handsome new building of two storeys high, and extending over upwards of 2,500 square yards of ground, and containing some of the largest and best appointed workshops in the district, the various departments of which are replete with all the best and most improved machinery, tools, and appliances that have been devised to effect economy in production and to secure perfect and uniform workmanship, and including circular and band saws, planing and tenoning machines, the latter taking off two sides of timber at one time ; circular moulding machine by Robinson & Son, Limited, of Rochdale ; grinding machinery for tools, &c. The works also contain a spacious suite of well-appointed offices and counting-house, together with extensive timber yard, well stocked with English and foreign timber, warehouse accommodation, a powerful steam-engine and boiler, and all the accessories of a large and thoroughly organised establishment. The firm have also a large store situated at Livesey Fold, Darwen. Mr. J. Westwell undertakes all kinds of joinery, building, and contractors' work, a leading speciality being the construction of school and church furniture, and in this line he has completed some of the largest contracts in the district. So complete are all the arrangements of the works, and the facilities afforded by the large amount of improved machinery at command, together with the number of skilled and experienced workmen regularly employed, that the firm stand in an unrivalled position to undertake and execute contracts and work of any magnitude at the shortest notice and with despatch and economy. The business in every department receives the strict personal attention of the proprietor, who never for a moment relaxes his exertions to maintain and extend the high reputation for first-class workmanship he has so well and firmly established. Mr. Joseph Westwell is well known and highly esteemed in Darwen and the neighbourhood, his long and thorough practical experience, sound judgment, and genial courtesy have secured his recognition in a wide sphere as an energetic and enterprising man, with whom it is pleasant and profitable to have business transactions.

Richard Bury, Junr., Engineer, &c., Dove Lane Engineering Works, Robin Bank, Darwen.—Although this business is one of comparatively recent origin, it has made rapid progress during the nine years it has been in existence, and has achieved a success that may be justly ascribed to the energy and ability with which it has been conducted. The Dove Lane engineering works consist principally of a large building of two storeys, and are admirably equipped with all the most modern and improved forms of patent machinery appliances, &c., motive power being supplied by a large engine of the latest construction. The work of the firm may be said to include all branches appertaining to the operations of engineers, millwrights, and general smiths ; but there are one or two branches in which special renown has been acquired. Thus, a large amount of work is done in connection with tram lines, and Mr. Bury is well known as the sole maker of Culter's Patent Snow Plough for work in this connection. Another special feature of the firm's productions consists of steam derricks for quarrymen and contractors, these being made of all capabilities from one ton upwards. In both these branches as in all other departments the firm have long been noted for excellent workmanship in construction and finish, and their productions can be relied upon as being second to none in durability and general merit. A large number of hands includes the most skilled and experienced workmen, and every branch of the work is carried out under the personal superintendence of the proprietor, who has a thoroughly practical knowledge of the trade in every detail, and is therefore enabled to ensure that degree of superiority that throughout has been so characteristic of the firm.

Timothy Bowling, Joiner, Builder and Cabinet-maker, Springfield Timber Yard and Saw Mills, Sough, Darwen.—Mr. Bowling has been actively engaged in this business for the past twelve years, and has acquired a name and reputation of far more than local celebrity. The works are very extensive and commodious, admirably constructed, and well arranged. The workshops are replete with all the best and most improved machinery, tools, and appliances that have been devised to effect economy in production and to secure perfect and uniform workmanship, including circular saws and morticing machines driven by steam power. The yard contains a large and comprehensive stock of timber suitable for the building trade and cabinet work, also building materials of all kinds. Mr. Bowling is well employed in every branch of the trade as joiner, builder and cabinet-maker, and gives employment to a staff of skilled and experienced workmen. So complete are all the arrangements of the works and the large amount of improved machinery at command, that the firm stands in a splendid position to undertake and execute orders and work of any magnitude on the shortest notice and with dispatch and economy. At Mr. Bowling's residence, No. 493, Bolton Road, are several large showrooms containing a large stock of furniture of the firm's own make, comprising dining, drawing and bedroom suites of elegant design and upholstered in the most fashionable materials; also kitchen furniture, strong, sound and durable. The whole of this stock is admirably arranged for ready reference and easy inspection, and for variety, improved design, and quality of materials, combined with sound and reliable workmanship, cannot be surpassed. The business in every department receives the strict personal attention of the proprietor, and is conducted throughout with marked ability, energy, and enterprise. Mr. T. Bowling is well-known and highly respected in business circles, and by his integrity, sound judgment, and genial courtesy, has acquired the confidence and support of a widespread and rapidly increasing connection.

J. Williamson, Wholesale Tea Dealer, 49, Market Street, Darwen.—This business has been in existence a great number of years, having been originally founded in 1848, when it was established by Mr. J. Williamson. During the whole of its career it has always held a foremost position in the trade, and has made continued and steady progress in every direction. The proprietor occupies a large and well-fitted establishment that includes a large double-fronted shop standing in a commanding position in Market Street. The trade carried on is that of grocer and general provision merchant, but special prominence is given to tea, a department in which the firm has long been renowned. Mr. Williamson makes this branch his particular study, and, being of long practical experience in the art of blending and tasting teas, he has acquired a first-class local reputation for the excellence of the goods in which he deals. He purchases the finest growths in the markets, and, by dealing on a large scale is enabled to supply his customers with a superior quality of tea at a very advantageous price. The premises include sample and store rooms, office, &c., and are thoroughly adapted to carrying on a large trade in tea. Mr. Williamson does a large wholesale business in tea, and not only in those varieties and blends of his own for which he is so renowned, but also in the well-known "Grandame's Garden Teas," for which he is the sole wholesale agent in this district. A very influential connection is maintained in all parts, and the firm is decidedly popular and successful.

Joseph Wilcock, Borough Mineral Water Works, Sudell Road, Darwen.—This business was established in 1850, in the present works, by Mr. R. Hummer, who carried it on until 1883, when it was acquired by Mr. Wilcock, the present proprietor. The premises are of large extent, the principal building measuring 100 feet by 50 feet, and there being a spacious yard with stabling and other outhouses. They are equipped in first-rate style with all the most approved modern machinery and appliances for producing those delicious aërated beverages for which the house has so long been famous. In addition to these the house has won a famous name for their celebrated British wines, including port and sherry, black-currant, blackberry, orange, and ginger, &c. The trade of the firm is very extensive, requiring the services of six horses and vans and a large staff of hands, and the business connection, which is of the most influential order, extends all over Darwen and many miles into the surrounding districts. The policy of sparing no expense where it can be applied in introducing new and improved machinery, and using only the purest and highest class of materials in the manufactures—a policy that has always characterised the management of this business—continues to maintain and extend the old-established reputation of the firm. Mr. Wilcock is well known in the trade. He is a frank, courteous gentleman, and his reputed upright principles have gained for him a high place in the esteem and confidence of his numerous warm supporters.

Geo. Rushton & Co., Brass Founders and Finishers, Mill Gap Brass Foundry, Bolton Road, Darwen.—This house, although of somewhat recent origin, has rapidly attained a prominent position in its particular class. The business was founded in 1883 and throughout has been worked upon sound principles that could hardly fail to command success and have achieved for the firm of Messrs. Rushton & Co. a widespread renown and an excellent reputation for superior work. The premises, which are well known under the title of the Mill Gap Brass Foundry, comprise a large and commodious building of two storeys, of which the upper floor consists of the fitting-shop and store-rooms. On the ground floor are the remaining workshops, foundry, &c., and the whole of the establishment is replete with all the most modern and improved forms of patent machinery. The staff varies somewhat according to the amount of work in hand, but there is always a considerable number of hands in constant employment. A large proportion of the work is done in connection with mill furnishing and repairing of mill fittings, &c., and a very influential connection is maintained among the leading millowners, &c. Among the chief specialities for the manufacture of which the firm are mostly renowned may be enumerated such as the improved sight-feed lubricators for steam-engines, iron and brass valves of all descriptions, improved steam and water taps, steam and water gauges, patent steam taps and reducing valves, gun-metal ball valves, self-feed valves for regulating the flow of size, &c. Brass and copper work of every description is also undertaken and carried out upon improved principles. The management of the firm is in the hands of Mr. Geo. Rushton, the principal, and under his able direction a very extensive business has been developed, not only in the immediate locality but also generally in all parts of the surrounding neighbourhood.

James Watson, General House Furnisher, 68 and 70, Duckworth Street, Darwen.—Among the most noted and prominent houses in the general house furnishing trade one of the principal in Darwen is that in the proprietorship of Mr. James Watson, who established the above business in 1873, since which date it has made very rapid progress and become widely known, not only in the immediate locality, but also generally in all parts of the district. The premises are well adapted to the requirements of an extensive trade. On the ground floor are the spacious show-rooms, elegantly fitted and commodiously arranged, the windows being effectively set out with a very fine display of household furniture in all varieties and of the best quality. Mr. Watson undertakes furnishing throughout, and his stock is extremely comprehensive in its nature. Special notice may be taken of the handsome drawing-room, dining-room, and bedroom suites, the latter being a great feature in which a large trade is done. There is also a very extensive and choice assortment of all classes of general hardware, tinware, ironmongery, Birmingham and Sheffield goods, &c. One of the most important branches is that of such goods as carpets, linoleum, and other descriptions of floor-cloth, for which this house has the reputation of being one of the cheapest in the town. Among the most noticeable specialities of the trade sewing machines form a particular item that deserves more than passing notice. Among the various goods in this department are the celebrated machines by "Bradbury," and also by the "Cherry-tree" Machine Company. Mr. Watson also offers a newly patented sewing machine called the "Cyclops," which exhibits many valuable improvements on the previous system, and has very rapidly acquired great popularity among the public generally. The most distinguishing feature of Mr. Watson's system of business is the adoption of the "hire system," which of late years has met with such favour. The system adopted by Mr. Watson is one based upon the soundest commercial principles, and its merit is admirably proved in the large trade that is done in this direction. The proprietor has devoted special attention to the quality of the goods, both as regards their construction and the material. In every branch the customer may rely upon receiving good value for outlay. A very large trade is done in all parts of Darwen and the neighbourhood within a considerable radius, and the firm is well known in all directions. Much of the success achieved may be justly attributed to the admirable management of the proprietor, who has conducted the business with marked energy and ability. He is well known and widely respected, and has been trustee of the Darwen Weavers' Association from its foundation years ago.

James Salmon, Tea and Coffee Merchant, Family Grocer, and Provision Merchant, 5, Bridge Street, Darwen.—This celebrated grocery business was acquired in 1860 by Mr. Salmon, who had been trained to the business from his youth, and for five years previously an assistant in the same house that he has guided with great business tact for nearly thirty years. The house has had a good reputation throughout the district as a grocery store for eighty years and more, and many a Darwen veteran can remember "Pearson's." The premises now occupied are large and commodious, and comprise sugar store, general grocery store, cheese and miscellaneous goods department, and tea depôt. Any attempt to accurately chronicle the various specialities that Mr. Salmon is constantly placing before his customers is far beyond our power, but Salmon's teas are renowned all over the district for their many excellences, and above all their great strength in liquor and fine aromatic flavour. The coffee is equally good and select, and such as must commend itself to every patron of the African berry. In sugars, too, the stock is particularly strong, including the best granulated, crystallized white crushed and superior loaf, all possessed of rare sweetening qualities. Packet and loose cocoa likewise appears in grand display, and is warranted the best. Then, again, in cheese all the best Cheshire and American brands are found in stock, together with prime home-cured hams and bacon and delicious dairy-made fresh butter, &c. The proprietor is a very large importer, especially of Irish butter, lard in skins and tins, foreign fruits of all kinds, spices, &c., being among the chief products received direct from the chief producers in the world. An extensive handling is also carried on in all sorts of table *bonnes-bouches*, such as jams, jellies, biscuits, various kinds, preserved meats, pickles, sauces, and such like besides *ad libitum*, to say nothing of such cereals as corn flour, arrowroot, tapioca, sago, rice, &c., of surpassing excellence in quality, as indeed are all the goods offered at this celebrated establishment. The custom is very extensive and well established. It may appropriately be added that Mr. Salmon's long and honourable connection with this branch of Darwen industry is the best evidence of the favour in which his business enterprise and ability are held by the general public.

Edwin Ainsworth, Funeral Undertaker, Coach-Builder and Wheelwright, 5, Victoria Street, Darwen.—Established thirty years ago by the late Mr. James Ainsworth at the present address, this business is now the property of that gentleman's son. The premises are of large extent, with large coach-houses and stabling for twenty-five horses in the rear. The shoeing forge and coach-building works are equipped with all the most approved modern machinery and appliances, including circular and other saws, moulding and planing machines, &c., which are driven by a powerful steam engine. Among the classes of work executed by the firm are the making of coffins in oak, pitch pine, and other materials; the making of every description of vehicles, repairing shandries, &c. In all departments of their business, including the shoeing of horses (which is carried on at their well-known Shorey Bank Shoeing Forge), the house does a large trade, being supported by the most influential families, contractors, and other owners of horses in the district. Special mention should be made of the firm's posting department, in which a large number of horses and vehicles of every kind are constantly employed, especially in the summer season; and the funeral undertaking department is warmly supported by the *élite* of the suburbs, and all classes of householders in Darwen. The energy and practical experience and honourable methods through which this business was formed, and the exceedingly moderate charges and promptitude in meeting urgent demands, continue to maintain and extend the old-established reputation of the firm. Mr. Ainsworth is a well-known gentleman, and his upright principles and agreeable, courteous manner have gained for him the same high place in the esteem and confidence of his numerous warm supporters so long enjoyed by his father.

Jacob Cooper, Coal and Lime Merchant, 2, Kay Street, Darwen.—As a coal and lime merchant Mr. Jacob Cooper established his business in Darwen many years ago, and as such he is now well known all over Lancashire. In connection with these departments of the business, Mr. Cooper, besides his Darwen premises, has branch establishments at Spring Vale and Blackburn stations, and in the sale of coal in Darwen alone, amongst householders, a good trade is done. The trade in lime is also extensive, and amongst other producers Mr. Cooper is the agent here for the Buxton Lime Company. Besides these departments of his business, Mr. Cooper is well known in influential circles as the sole agent in Darwen for the Bridgwater Canal Trustees, a position of great importance, and in connection with which his agreeable, courteous demeanour and honourable principles have won for him a high place in the esteem and confidence of the commercial gentlemen here.

Samuel Pearson, Darwen Paperhanging Warehouse, Church Street, Darwen.—Mr. Samuel Pearson established his business here in 1876, first as a managing partner of the firm of Alston & Co., and since 1885 in his own name. The premises are stone-built, three storeys high, and with a most handsome and elegant elevation. The upper floor and a large building at the rear are used as warehouses, and a very large and varied stock is always kept on hand. The large windows make a most excellent display of the most costly and elaborate wall papers in the very latest and most tasteful patterns and designs brought out by the trade. Few branches of British industry have made greater strides in advance during the past few years than our wall paper stainers, and Mr. Pearson is in a position to supply his patrons with the very latest and best goods in gold, bronze, &c., as soon as they are produced, so that his large windows, facing the Market Hall, are always graced with the latest triumphs of art in this now very important branch of business. He acts as special agent for Messrs. C. & J. G. Potter, of the Belgrave Works, Darwen, the most extensive manufacturers of wall papers in the kingdom. He does a very large trade in this department, and he also carries on a considerable business as a general paper merchant, a large assortment of browns, glazeds, casings, and other numerous varieties being always in stock. The whole business is under Mr. Pearson's own control and superintendence, and he displays the greatest industry, energy, and enterprise in his careful management of the concern.

J. Wardley & Son, Printers, &c., Market Street, Darwen. —This business was established in 1838 by a Mr. Edward Gregson, who carried on a very thriving trade as printer by the ordinary method of manual press. When Mr. Wardley took over the business he extended the scope of the work by the addition of steam power to letterpress and lithographic printing, and the firm now ranks among the foremost of its kind. The premises occupied are admirably adapted to the requirements of the trade, and are situated in one of the best positions in the town, between Church Street and Church Bank Street, the work being approached by an archway just below the Darwen Theatre Royal. The whole of the premises are fitted up with the most improved and latest type of modern machinery and plant, the motive power being supplied from a large water ram-engine of the latest construction and steam-engine and boiler. The firm do a large amount of printing work of all descriptions, principally of a commercial kind, in which they have an extensive and valuable connection in all parts of Darwen. They devote particular attention to the requirements of football and cricket clubs, and are doing a considerable amount of work in printing match cards (for either pocket or window), subscription cards, admission tickets, &c. They are also renowned for their leviathan posters, most of these being for football and cricket purposes, also. All orders are executed with the most commendable punctuality and despatch, and the work is carried out upon the very best principles. The stationery department of the business, which is a very important feature, is confined exclusively to commercial requisites, and forms a highly flourishing branch in which a large trade is done. The business is very ably conducted, and the firm is widely known, the senior partner being a member of the Town Council of Darwen, the chairman of the Market Committee, and secretary of the Central Liberal Club.

Abraham Altham, Tea Dealer, Market Street, Darwen, and Victoria Street, Blackburn.—There are few names more widely known in the tea trade so far as the North of England is concerned than that of "Abraham Altham," under which title the above branch establishment is carried on with so much success. Mr. Abraham Altham commenced business in Burnley, and exhibited a great amount of enterprise in his system of developing trade, being one of the first that introduced the system of giving useful presents to the purchasers of tea. The rapid increase of the business of the above firm was so marked that the proprietor found it necessary to open branch establishments in nearly all the important towns in the North of England, and thus it is not too much to say that few houses ever commanded such a widespread trade. Lancashire especially is a county in which the name is widely known, there being a great number of branches here. The founder of this firm is now dead, and the business is very ably carried on upon the same lines by his executors. Mr. Altham was widely popular in Burnley, a town of which he was a native and eventually a magistrate. The branch establishment in Darwen is located in a good position in Market Street. It comprises a large shop that is heavily stocked with a variety of goods incidental to the operations of tea dealers, &c. A noticeable feature of the window display is the choice assortment of presents, which embrace a variety of useful and ornamental articles, cases of birds, vases, and domestic articles too numerous to mention. The chief speciality so far as the trade is concerned is a famous blend of Indian teas known as the "Indian Favourite." It is largely in demand among the better class of customers and is undoubtedly a tea that is unsurpassed in flavour at the price by any in the market. All goods are of the very best quality, and here, as in all the other branches, a very high standard of excellence has been maintained.

Entwisle & Nutter, General Ironmongers and Merchants, Market Street, Darwen.—A premier establishment in the line of commerce and manufacture above alluded to is that of Messrs. Entwisle & Nutter, the founders and sole proprietors, the business having been established by them at this address in 1849. The edifice is three storeys in height, and an imposing street frontage of three windows, each containing a large variety of goods, conspicuous among which appears a splendid display of marble mantelpieces, for which the house has a high reputation all over Lancashire. Great care is taken in the production of these mantels; they are original and exquisite in design, and beautiful in finish. There is also another branch of manufacturing industry worthily represented by the house—viz., screw-bolt making—which is carried on to a large extent at their works in High Street, where a most efficient plant is found, embracing all the most modern improvements in machinery and other appliances for the production of these bolts, and in addition to machinery the firm employ a large staff of experienced hands. The driving power for the various drills, &c., is derived from a well-constructed horizontal engine and boiler, the general aspect of the works being the *ne plus ultra* of what a bolt manufactory should be. Passing on to the executive part of the ironmongery business, it should be noticed that all kinds of whitesmith's, bell-hanging, tinplate, and gasfitting work are executed in the best possible manner by picked tradesmen, the firm members carefully superintending all work done under their auspices, and generally directing the organisation of the business. The trade is very extensive, and well established among the principal builders and others in the town and district.

Messrs. Leonard Bros., Fish, Game, Poultry, and Fruit Salesmen, 9, Bridge Street, Darwen, and 1, Fish Market, Blackburn.—One of the principal shops to be found in the above-mentioned trade in the neighbourhood of Darwen is that of the firm referred to in the title to this notice, the business having been established at this address in 1887. The firm have also a mart at No. 1, Fish Market, Blackburn, where an extensive trade is carried on. The premises occupied in Bridge Street consist of a double-fronted shop on the ground floor of a two-storey edifice in the most frequented part of this popular thoroughfare, a few doors above the Circus. The business done is exclusively high-class. The stock always kept on hand consists of all the best kinds of fish, game, and poultry, the quality of which can be guaranteed. The fish is received in large and frequent consignments from the principal fisheries of the United Kingdom. The poultry, too, is obtained direct from the leading farmsteads in the vicinity of the town, and can therefore always be relied upon for freshness and good flavour. Then, again, during the shooting season daily consignments of all the choicest descriptions of game are received from the English and Scotch moors. The fish trade is a speciality of the house, the spacious window nearest the Circus being devoted to the display of goods in that line, a very prominent feature being lobsters, crabs, native oysters, &c., of which there is usually a large assortment. The window on the other side of the entrance also invariably shows a splendid display of the choicest fruit in season, such as English and foreign grapes and the rarer kinds of fruit to be found only at a first-class fruiterer's. The game, too, immense quantities of which are hung across the front of the premises, constitute an important branch of the business, the whole of which is particularly well organised. Several assistants are employed, together with spring carts

for the delivery of goods to customers, who are likewise waited upon for orders by request. The trade is very extensive and well-established among the best families in the town and neighbourhood. The firm members are gentlemen of great experience in all branches of the business, and highly esteemed by all with whom they have commercial transactions.

Henry Cooper & Son, Furniture Dealers, &c., 267, Bolton Road, Darwen.—This business was established in 1880 by Mr. Henry Cooper at premises higher up in Bolton Road to those the firm now occupy, Mr. Cooper removing thence to the present address in 1881. Up to a recent period Mr. Henry Cooper was the sole principal, but he has now taken his son into the concern as a partner, and the style has been altered accordingly. The firm are dealers in new and second-hand furniture of every description, also dealers in wringing machines, &c., and their trade is of very large proportions. The emporium—267, Bolton Road—is a handsome stone structure, two storeys high, and having a frontage of 27 feet, and possessing a fine elevation, which gives it a prominent and commanding appearance in contrast with properties in the vicinity; and we may observe, in passing, that in 1888 Mr. Cooper became the purchaser of this property, together with the plot of land adjoining. The premises are admirably adapted to the requirements of the firm's business, and are fitted up in excellent style. The stock is of great magnitude, and the display of bedsteads in brass, wood, and iron is very imposing. All descriptions of furniture may be obtained here, from the very best qualities downwards, and we may remark that wringing machines form a leading feature of the firm's trade. Owing to the large purchases which Messrs. Cooper & Son make from time to time of furniture of all kinds, both new and second-hand, they are always able to offer intending purchasers at their establishment decided bargains, and the knowledge of this fact accounts in no small degree for the very large patronage which the firm enjoys from all classes of the community. The business is conducted on strictly honourable and straightforward lines, and no concern in the town or district is more popular, or more liberally supported by the general public.

T. Lindsey, Photographer, &c., 43, Duckworth Street, Darwen.—The establishment is not only the chief artistic photographic repository in Darwen, but the studio is fully equal to any that can be met with in Lancashire, and is conducted upon the highest principles. Mr. Lindsey founded the business in 1885, having previously acquired a thoroughly practical and sound knowledge of photography in Peterborough. His work is first-class, and would not easily be equalled and certainly not surpassed by any provincial photographer in the kingdom. Mr. Lindsey makes a great speciality of enamelled photos, and work on porcelain, a branch to which he has devoted particular attention. In all the general departments of the work he is particularly noted for the artistic merit of the grouping, and his work has attracted much attention by its beauty of execution and finish. The premises are thoroughly adapted to the requirements of a first-class business, and in every detail are admirably appointed. The lighting arrangements of the studios are perfect, the fittings, &c., are of the best kind, and no expense has been spared in order to ensure the very highest class of work. Mr. Lindsey is also an artist of considerable ability in the production of oil-paintings, and has executed some really excellent work in this direction. In addition to the branches of business thus indicated, Mr. Lindsey does a large trade in all manner of high-class fancy goods, porte-monnaies, &c., &c., and has a large stock and very elegant display of handsome articles of all descriptions. The business is well known, and is one of the foremost of its kind in England.

J. Eccles, Pianoforte Warehouse, Victoria Buildings, Market Street, Darwen.—This business has been conducted with great success by Mr. Eccles for many years, and he is probably one of the best-known musicians throughout the locality. He is particularly renowned as the promoter, manager, and musical conductor of a series of high-class subscription concerts, held periodically in Darwen, and celebrated for miles round as "J. Eccles' Subscription Concerts." He is also the honorary local examiner for the Royal College of Music, London, and likewise holds the appointment as organist of Market Street Congregational Church, in Farnworth, near Bolton. Mr. Eccles is also well known for his abilities as a composer; among his numerous productions one of the most popular being the anthem, "Praise ye the Lord," which is sung in all parts of the kingdom. His premises at the above address comprise a spacious and elegantly fitted saloon, stocked with a choice assortment of musical instruments of all kinds. Pianofortes are a leading feature, and there is a large stock of both these and American organs, all by the most renowned and reliable makers. There is also a first-class supply of violins, violas, wood-wind and brass instruments, and all other necessaries for the complete equipment of either string or military band. A large trade is done in sheet music of the latest publication, the stock being extremely varied and extensive. The whole of the appointments of the establishment, as well as all the details of the management, are those pertaining to a high-class musical depot; and it is one of the most widely patronised and popular houses of its kind in Lancashire. A very large trade and connection have been developed, and the success that has attended the career of this business may be justly attributed to the energy and conspicuous ability exhibited in the management.

E. C. Beet, Musical Instrument Depot, &c., Handel House, The Circus, Darwen.—This noted musical instrument depot, which is the oldest in Darwen, was founded by Mr. Beet in 1863, consequently it has enjoyed a career of upwards of a quarter of a century. Mr. Beet is a dealer in and repairer of all kinds of musical instruments —brass, reed, and string—and he likewise keeps a very extensive assortment of pianos, harmoniums, American organs, &c. He is agent for the sale of the celebrated " Karn Organ," manufactured by Messrs. D. W. Karn & Co., of Woodstock, Ontario, Canada, which has gained a worldwide repute, also Bell and Co.'s organs. These instruments are adapted to a great variety of uses, and they can be obtained of any compass and power to meet every requirement, and every organ is warranted by the makers for seven years from date of manufacture. The stock of pianos is a first-class one, and embraces instruments by all the leading makers, English and foreign. He is sole agent for Squire & Longson's Cremona pianos, Brooklyn piano, Kirkman piano, Geo. Russell & Co.'s transposing piano, Justin Browne's pianos, Rogers' pianos, and many other high-class makers. Handel House is always an object of great attraction to the public, and especially the musical section of it, inasmuch as the display of instruments of every description is most imposing. Mr. Beet has a very widespread connection, and he does an extensive trade in letting out pianos, &c., on hire and likewise on the three years' purchase system. Being a thoroughly practical business man in his profession he personally superintends all the repairs to pianos and other instruments, and he is also a most competent tuner of pianos, a fact which must be clearly seen from the very flattering testimonials he has received from local pianists and London manufacturers, one of which we here mention. " Testimonial.—237 and 239, Euston Road, London, May 2, 1870. I can with confidence testify to the practical knowledge and experience of Mr. E. C. Beet, of Darwen, as a tuner and repairer, and especially recommend him to persons who have pianos of my manufacture, feeling assured they will be done justice to at his hands. Signed, Justin Browne, Pianoforte Manufacturer, 237 and 239, Euston Road, London." And is very largely patronised. We may mention the fact that pianos can be purchased from Mr. Beet by instalments as low as 10s. 6d. per month, and harmoniums from 6s. per month. His emporium is also a published music repository, and sheet music of all descriptions —including the very latest compositions—can always be obtained thereat on the best terms. He keeps a staff of experienced assistants, and all orders are executed with care and promptitude. We will only add that his business is conducted in a manner which gives universal satisfaction to his clients, and his honourable and straightforward mode of dealing has not only secured him a valuable trade, but has won for him the goodwill and esteem of his fellow-citizens.

Richard Timperley, Photographic Artist, &c., 27 and 29, Bridge Street, Darwen.—In 1858 the firm of Richard and Henry T. Timperley was founded, as printers, stationers, fancy repository proprietors, photographers, and artists, the two brothers uniting to a technical knowledge of the printing trade a high artistic skill, by which they were able to add to their already extensive business a splendid photographic connection. For many years the firm had a considerable connection and repute all over the country for the production of coloured letterpress printing. In 1876 Richard Timperley invented and patented a successful machine for printing in four colours at one operation of the sheet. This machine gave a great impetus to their business and a world-wide connection. From the first Mr. R. Timperley had charge also of the post-office at Darwen, and he conducted that department of her Majesty's service continuously up to the date of the dissolution of the partnership, in 1883, when the post-office became connected with Mr. Henry T. Timperley, by whom it is still administered with conspicuous ability. Mr. Richard Timperley continued the printing, publishing, and decoration business at his Bankside Printing Works. In 1888 he opened a business as photographer and dealer in artists' materials, &c., in Bridge Street. This establishment is situated in one of the best and busiest parts of Darwen. In this year, through failing health Mr. Timperley disposed of his printing business to the *Darwen Post* Newspaper Company, but he still retained the church decoration business, which is continued at his Bridge Street address, where he also carries on a wholesale and retail stationery business, and holds a large and comprehensive stock of stationery requisites, which is fully representative of the trade in all its branches. Picture frames of every kind are also made on the premises, and the best English gilt frames made and pier glasses re-gilt. The premises are of handsome and attractive appearance, with exceptionally fine frontage. The shop contains a very fine selection of works of art, paintings, both in oil and water colours, and photographs, which exhibit in every detail the superior skill and talent employed in this establishment. The studio is situated on the top floor, and is admirably lighted and furnished with the best scientific apparatus and appliances known to the photographic profession. Mr. R. Timperley finds the artistic pursuits in which he is now so extensively engaged most congenial to his taste and quite sufficient to occupy the whole of his time. It is no flattery or exaggeration to state that there are few men better known or more highly esteemed in Darwen, and by his well-known ability, sound judgment, and genial courtesy Mr. Richard Timperley has secured the confidence and support of a very high-class and valuable connection.

R. Green & Sons, Boot and Shoe Warehouse, Green Street, Darwen.—One of the most eminent and fashionable boot and shoe establishments in the town is that of Messrs. R. Green and Sons, who commenced business some twenty-six years ago. The mart is centrally situated, well appointed, and has an attractive street frontage, there being a commodious workshop, fitted with an excellent working plant of modern machinery, and where, in addition, a full staff of experienced workmen are regularly employed. In the measure department especial regard is paid to the structure of the foot, whereby an easy and elegant fit is ensured with the same attention to economy as if selected from the stock. However, it must be of paramount importance to note that the whole of the firm's immense stock of boots and shoes are of superior quality, and the house being undoubtedly one of the best in the trade. Messrs. Green & Sons organise their business routine with the definite object of providing for the upper, middle and working-classes, an establishment where fashionably-made, and at the same time durable, boots and shoes can be obtained at small cost, comparatively speaking, a fact which is daily verified by the numerous customers who throng this establishment. Moreover, they supply measured goods at the same price as from stock, and everything is done to promote the prompt and expeditious execution of all orders, their entire working and commercial staff being about twenty hands, while the firm members carefully superintend all work, with a view to protecting the high reputation the house has attained in all branches of the boot and shoe trade. The retail department is particularly well worth inspection, as the house has always on hand excellent value in ladies' and gentlemen's wear, as well as a large assortment of juvenile goods, the quality and high-class finish of which will be readily appreciated when seen. The bespoke department has special attention, and having given so much satisfaction in regard to quality of work, exactness in fitting, and promptness of execution, has greatly increased. This embraces all ordinary as well as hand-sewn gentlemen's top boots, hunting boots, walking shoes, &c., and will justify any confidence placed in them. The trade, though local, is extensive and well-established. All the partners are practical tradesmen and gentlemen of the highest commercial status and integrity.

R. Nightingale, Cabinet Maker, House Furnisher, &c., Bowling Green Mill, Darwen.—This extensive business, which is undoubtedly one of the largest and most popular in the district, was originally established in Grimshaw Street. In 1881, owing to its rapid development and the necessity for increased accommodation, the present extensive and commodious premises were acquired. The main building is of stone, four storeys high, and having a frontage of fully 100 feet. The sale-rooms are on the ground floor, and run the whole length of the building. There is also a large detached workshop, where a number of skilled and experienced workmen are busily employed in making furniture of all kinds, also in undertakers' work, &c. The whole of the furniture is hand made, and of thoroughly seasoned materials and sound and reliable workmanship. The stock in the warehouse and showrooms is very large and comprehensive, being replete with all the best features of the various lines engaged in, and comprises every article necessary for complete house furnishing. Mr. R. Nightingale has most successfully introduced into this district the hire system of purchase, by which many hundreds of families have been enabled to furnish their houses in a far better and much more comfortable manner than formerly, and at an easy rate of payment which they scarcely feel. Wringing and washing machines are also supplied on the same system. Mr. Nightingale has also added a news agency and stationery department to his business, all the leading London and provincial dailies and the popular periodicals being on sale. The business in every department receives the strict personal attention of the proprietor, and is conducted throughout with marked ability, energy, and enterprise. Mr. R. Nightingale possesses the advantage of long and thorough practical experience, and his well-known integrity, sound judgment, and genial courtesy have secured his recognition in a wide sphere as a man with whom it is pleasant and profitable to have business transactions.

S. C. Cartridge & Co., Merchant Tailors, Clothiers, and Juvenile Outfitters, Market Street and School Street, Darwen.— This business, which is one of the foremost of the kind in Darwen, was carried on for many years by Mr. Eccles, and was acquired in 1885 by Mr. Cartridge, by whom the premises were greatly enlarged and remodelled. Occupying a handsome building of three storeys in height, the premises are probably the largest in the trade in this district of England. They are most tastefully fitted up on the ground floor; sale shop, cutting and fitting establishments on second floor, the workrooms and other warehouses being situated on the floors above. The classes of goods displayed comprise all the most fashionable patterns in tweeds and other cloths, all being of the highest quality, as well as a valuable stock of juvenile outfits which belong chiefly to the wholesale department. As bespoke tailors of the first order, this firm is well known in the trade, and their perfectly fitting and stylish products has won for the proprietor a high reputation. Mr. Cartridge is an agreeable, courteous gentleman, who has gained the well-deserved position he enjoys by hard work and honourable methods in the management of his business, which have also won for him a high place in the esteem and confidence of all with whom he meets in business, whether as a buyer or seller.

John Crook, Spring Vale Brewery, Over Darwen.— The extensive business carried on by Mr. John Crook, wholesale ale and porter brewer, at the Spring Vale Brewery, Over Darwen, is probably the most thoroughly representative of its kind in the district. Establishe originally by Mr. William Crook, the business, after changing hands several times, ultimately passed into the possession of the present proprietor, Mr. John Crook. The premises are very extensive, and at the same time compact and complete in every detail. The buildings are handsome; a five-storey brick tower in the centre forms a pleasing and attractive feature. The brewery throughout is admirably constructed and well arranged; the various departments are replete with machinery and appliances embodying all the latest improvements and the most comprehensive utilities. The operations are conducted on the most approved principles, with the additional advantage of thorough practical experience. The firm brew both pale and mild ales, stout, and porter, made from pure malt and hops only, which for purity, strength, and flavour cannot be surpassed. In addition to the brewery proper the premises contain extensive storage accommodation for malt and hops, the latter coming mostly from Kent and Sussex, also spacious and well-appointed offices, general and private, large and well-constructed cellars, engine

and boiler-house, and all the accessories of a large and thoroughly organised establishment. This brewery has a very great advantage in the splendid supply of water, which, both by scientific chemical analysis and practical experience, is proved to be admirably adapted to the purpose of brewing, and quite equal to that of the celebrated London and Burton breweries. With such essentials, then, as pure English malt and hops, good and suitable water, and thorough practical experience, there is little wonder that the ales and porter brewed at the Spring Vale Brewery have acquired such a widespread celebrity, and are rapidly growing more and more in popular favour. In addition to the extensive wholesale business in supplying public-houses, hotels, restaurants, &c., Mr. Crook has developed a large and increasing trade in bottled ales and stout, and has also a high-class family connection, supplying ale, beer, and stout in nine-gallon casks for private use. The business in every department receives the strict personal attention of the proprietor, and is conducted throughout with marked ability, energy, and enterprise. The extensive cellarage accommodation enables the firm to store large quantities of their celebrated ales and stout, and they make it a rule to send out that only which is in a clear, sound, and thoroughly matured condition, and best calculated to give the greatest satisfaction to their customers, and to maintain and extend the high reputation they have so firmly established.

John Knowles, Quarry Owner, Joiner, Builder, and Contractor, Darwen.—Mr. John Knowles commenced business in 1845, and by sheer perseverance, aided by that good fortune which generally comes to the aid of an honest and determined man, has raised himself to an eminence in his business which can only be attained by few. Mr. Knowles's workshops are situated in what is locally known as Water Lane, a road leading by the rear of the Darwen Paper Mills towards Sandhills. Here an immense timber industry is carried on, the saw mills alone, with the joiners' and other shops belonging thereto, occupying a space of over an acre. The saw mills contain tenoning, moulding, morticing, and planing machines in every variety known to the trade. There are several

band and circular saws, the whole being propelled by a horizontal engine. The Bolton Road timber yards of Mr. John Knowles, containing many thousand feet of British and foreign timber, are well known to the people of Darwen as the most extensive in the town. Mr. John Knowles is also the proprietor of two extensive stone quarries; one at Thorny Height, the other at Radford, some little distance from the town. These quarries are celebrated for their output of ashlar, longstone copings, flags, &c. There are scarcely any contracts of consequence for large building undertakings in this neighbourhood which are not entrusted to the proprietor of this business. A working staff of a hundred and fifty hands are employed here; and a fact well known and freely admitted is, that from the taking out of a foundation to the laying of the last slate on the roof Mr. John Knowles is completely master of the situation.

John Thomas Nuttall, Accountant, Insurance Broker, and Commission Agent, 6, Railway Road, Darwen.—The business of the accountant, insurance and commission agent is notably represented in Darwen in the well-known firm of John Thomas Nuttall, whose premises are situated in Railway Road. Mr. Nuttall has recently bought Lower Wood Bank, late residence of Mr. James Garstang, cotton manufacturer, and having made exte sive alterations is now residing there. His present business establishment consists of a handsome office, which is situated in the ground floor of the fine block occupied by the Theatre buildings, and opposite the new Market House, which is the finest public building in Darwen. The office is admirably furnished, and in it an extensive accountancy, insurance, and commission business is carried on. The principal firms for which Mr. Nuttall is an insurance broker and general commission agent are Messrs. Booth & Openshaw, oil and tallow refiners, sizing materials, &c., Blackburn; F. B. Welch & Co., engineers, millwrights, &c., of Manchester; Blackman Air Propeller Co.; Queen Insurance Co.; Equitable Accident Co.; Guardian Plate Glass; Lancashire and Yorkshire Accident and Employers' Liability Insurance Co.; Boiler Insurance and Steam Power Co., Limited; and the Imperial Live Stock Association. For each of these firms Mr. Nuttall does a large business in and around Darwen, among commercial and manufacturing houses of the most influential order. Having an agreeable, courteous manner, Mr. Nuttall, who is a well-known gentleman, is much respected by his numerous warm supporters.

H. J. & A. Coulthurst, Engineers, Robert Street, Darwen.—This business, which exhibits in a marked degree the results of well applied energy and enterprise, is carried on in a large two-storeyed building, thoroughly equipped with all the necessary machines, among the chief items of which are lathes, planing, shaping, boring, and other machines, together with steam hammers, &c. The motive-power is provided by an engine of modern construction, made by the firm and therefore fully adapted to all requirements. The firm are busily employed in all branches of work incidental to the operations of engineers, millwrights, iron and brass founders, and are particularly noted for a speciality in sanitary pipe machines, a branch of engineering to which they have devoted great attention. They supply many of the most renowned houses in the trade. Among the other departments to which they devote particular attention it may be mentioned that they are noted as makers of pumps for collieries and paper mills; they also re-bore cylinders and fit them with all kinds of metallic pistons; make iron and brass castings of every description, and do a large amount of work in moulding spur, bevel, and worm wheels by machinery. They are inventors of a new moulding machine specially designed for the rapid moulding of small wheels from segments. Also patentees of improved flanges and the mode of cutting same as applied to metallic pipes. With the introduction of these flanges they get a better and safer way of making the joints. They require fewer bolts than usual; and the rings, which are supplied by the firm, are much cheaper than the old ones. They supply various kinds of rings to meet the requirements of paper makers, manufacturing chemists, &c. The cost is much lower than the ordinary pipe, and it is believed they will in a very short time entirely supersede the old method of pipe making. All work is completed upon the most approved principles, the hands employed are selected from among the most skilled and experienced artisans, and every department is under the careful superintendence of the principals of the firm, who have developed a very extensive and flourishing trade in all parts of the locality. The connection is highly important, and as an instance of this it may be mentioned that the firm do all the work of an engineering character required by the Corporation of Darwen.

Pieces from the Papers

DARWEN.

A DARWEN BUILDER FINED.—At the Borough Petty Sessions, held on Thursday afternoon, James Jackson, builder, Snape-street, Darwen, was fined 10s and costs for being drunk. Defendant said he had been robbed of several articles whilst he was drunk, and he was advised to get the aid of the police in tracing the lost property.

DARWEN TOWN COUNCIL.—At the quarterly meeting of the Town Council, held on Thursday afternoon, the Mayor (Councillor E. M. Davies) occupied the chair. Amongst matters upon the agenda paper was the recommendation of the Gas Committee to raise the gas manager's salary from £280 to £330 per annum, and the committee also suggested that in future Mr. Duxbury should devote the whole of his time to gas business and not have the charge of the water department as well.—A long discussion ensued upon this recommendation, and eventually the Council decided by 12 votes to six to support the suggestion of the committee.—It was also decided to build entirely new stables instead of altering those used at present at the old workhouse.

PRESENTATION TO SUPERINTENDENT NOBLETT.—On Thursday afternoon there was a large attendance of the borough justices and the general public at the Police-court, Duckworth-street, upon the occasion of a testimonial, consisting of a purse containing 60 guineas and an address, being presented to Superintendent Noblett, who has been recently promoted and transferred from Darwen to Widnes.—The Mayor (Mr. E. M. Davies), in handing the purse to Superintendent Noblett, congratulated him upon his promotion, which, he said, was well deserved. During the five and a half years he had been stationed at Darwen he had given universal satisfaction.—Mr. Noblett sincerely thanked all for the kind manner in which he had been treated, and said the address would be handed down as an heirloom to his family.—Superintendent Myers and Inspector Leeming were also present.

BLACKBURN.
NOTES BY THE WAY.

BLACKBURN SAYINGS AND DOINGS.

As will be gathered from the letter read at the quarterly meeting of the Town Council on Thursday, Mr.
H. M. Stanley does not intend to visit Blackburn this
year. It was understood that the Blackburn Literary
Club had arranged with the eminent traveller to deliver a
lecture in Blackburn sometime next month, and the Corporation therefore intended to officially recognise the
visit. However, Mr. Stanley, owing to his recent illness
needs more rest and quiet, and next week he and Mrs.
Stanley leave for Switzerland. From thence they proceed
to America where Mr. Stanley has several lecturing en-
gagements which will keep him in that country for
some time.

One or two interesting topics were ventilated at the
Council meeting on Thursday, and in the course of the
two or three discussions which took place a few of the
members tried their hands at witty speechmaking with
a success which might, perhaps, be considered of an un-
gratifying kind. The question of the increase of the
wages of the clerks in the Town Clerk's office, together
with the fixing of a maximum amount, was the first to
come under discussion.

Councillor Hamer, who generally likes to hear the
sweet music of his own voice, thinking that a precedent
was being formed, and that the idea of an increase might
become contagious in all the corporate departments,
asked for an explanation. This the Mayor vouchsafed,
denying that the Corporation were creating a precedent,
and stating that the clerks in question deserved all the
money they got—a sentiment which met with a cor-
dial approval from the whole Council, with two notable
exceptions.

Alderman Whiteley, in one of his most jocular moods,
and in a speech bristling with words of thundering
sound, condemned the expenditure on the new retiring
rooms for the members of the different committees. His
descriptions of the furniture and the decorations were
as brilliant and as elaborate as the subjects with which
he was dealing. He paid special attention to Councillor
Eastwood, the erstwhile economist of the Council, but
who, since he had assumed the responsibilities of the
chairman of the Town Hall Committee, had thrown all
his notions of thrift to the winds and embraced with
even a more ardent affection the most extravagant ten-
dencies.

No less tender was Councillor Hamer with Councillor
Eastwood, whom he denounced as the most extravagant
chairman the Town Hall Committee had ever been blessed
with. The sarcasm seemed to be infectious, for Councillor Hamer followed in the same strain as Alderman
Whiteley, and, after condemning the expense as unjusti-
fiable, recommended that notepaper with stamps thrown
in, as well as coffee and cigars, should be provided free
of expense for those councillors whose privilege it was to
use the room.

To his credit be it said, Councillor Eastwood received
all this bantering without a shade of annoyance, and
when his turn came he made his explanation. He
pointed out that the greater portion of the expense had
not been for the furnishing of the room, but
in its construction, which he said some members had thought was impossible to make. He urged
that true economy was in getting full value for their
money, a statement with which few people will find
fault.

This (Saturday) afternoon the annual sports in connection with the East Lancashire Cricket Club take
place in the Alexandria Meadows. Given fine weather,
the meet ought to be a thorough success, inasmuch as a
large number of entries, including those of some of the
leading athletes of the country, have been received.

GRAMMAR SCHOOL OF QUEEN ELIZABETH,
BLACKBURN.

Head Master.....................Mr. T. AINSWORTH, M.A.

Asistant Masters ....{ Mr. T. J. SYCKILMOORE, B.A.
Mr. W. A. HAWORTH, A.A.
Mr. JAS. BRIGGS.

French Master ....Mons. J. A. MERCHIER, B.A.
Science Mastership (vacant).

Preparation for Business, for Preliminary Examinations in
connection with Law, Medicine, &c., and for Matriculation at
the Universities.

The next Term will begin Monday, September 15.

DARWEN.

THE MAYORALTY.—The Mayor (Councillor Ernest
Morgan Davies, J.P.) has signified his willingness to
occupy the civic chair during the ensuing 12 months.
This will be his second year of office. Councillor Gillibrand, the only Conservative representative in the Council, signed the requisition asking Mr. Davies to allow himself to be nominated for the mayoralty.

WIFE ASSAULT.—Richard Harwood, quarryman, 4,
Junction-street, was yesterday, at the Borough Police-
court, charged with assaulting his wife Mary, who is
now residing at 8, Eccles-row. Defendant was bound
over to keep the peace for six months, and a separation
order was granted, Mrs. Harwood stating that her husband had beaten her several times previously.

NEW LIBERAL CLUB.—The ceremony of laying the
foundation-stone of the new Liberal Club at Whitehall
was performed on Saturday afternoon by Mrs. C. P.
Huntington, wife of the Liberal candidate. The club will be
known as the Bright Reform Club, and is situate at the
junction of Park-road and Bolton-road. Mr. F. G. Hindie
presided at the afternoon proceedings, but at the entertainment in the Co-operative Hall in the evening Mr. C.
P. Huntington occupied the chair and delivered an address. The contract for the new building has been let to
Mr. Knowles.

HEALTH REPORT.—For the month ending August 31st'
the Medical Officer (Dr. Armitage) reports that the
health of the borough continues good. The were 101
births, viz., 56 males and 45 females, or a birth-rate of
33·2 per 1,000. The rate for the same period last year
was 33·0. Last month 51 deaths were recorded, or a
death-rate of 16·7. The death-rate last year was 13·5.
Seven deaths ensued from zymotic diseases, viz., scarlet
fever 1, whooping cough 1, and diarrhœa 5.

SLEEPING OUT.—At the County Police-court, yesterday, James Miller, tramp, was charged with sleeping in
a cabin near the ironworks, Eccleshill.—P.C. Eckersley
said that he found defendant asleep about 11 o'clock on
Monday night.—Defendant, in answer to Mr. Greenway,
said that permission had been given him to sleep there,
and in support of this called Mr. James Boyd, store
minder, Darwen Ironworks.—Mr. Greenway considered
that Mr. Boyd had tacitly consented to defendant sleeping on the premises, and said his decision was that defendant had better get out of Darwen as fast as he could,
and not let the police find him in the town at all. He
should get away.—Defendant: I will, sir. I am exceedingly
obliged to you. Thank you all, gentlemen.

DARWEN.

ROMAN CATHOLIC MISSION.—During the last fortnight
a mission has been conducted at St. Joseph's Catholic
Church, by the Rev Fathers Bannon and Howell (Re-
demptorists), of Liverpool. The services have been
remarkably well attended; at those held in the evening
the church has been filled to overflowing, the chancel as
well as the body of the church being filled. On Thursday evening Father Bannon was the preacher.

AMUSING SCENE IN COURT.—At the Borough Police-
court, Ainsworth Ainsworth, farmer, Tockholes, was
summoned for allowing his dog to be at large un-
muzzled.—The constable said he had seen defendant's
dog fully 200 yards from his house, on the Tockholes
road. The dog ran home, and he followed it, and told
defendant he would be reported.—Defendant: It's a lie.
The policeman is telling complete lies in order to make
it into a case.—The Clerk: You are not doing yourself
any good behaving like that. It's not proper respect to
the magistrates.—Defendant: Well, I dare say not.—Mr.
Potter (chairman): Have you anything to say to the
Bench?—Defendant: Well, chaps, this is the first time
as ever I've been among such like fellows. Do as weel
as yo' can wi' it. It's the very first time that I've ever
been inside a court-house. I've told you my tale. He
has been telling complete lies. That's all I've got to
say. I've done. and I'm not going to tell lies on purpose. You can please yourself.—Mr. Potter: Do you
say the dog was not outside your yard?—Defendant:
It was not outside the yard at all, never. I were feeding
the poultry when he coom up.—Mr. Potter: Did he
bring the dog with him?—Defendant: When he coom
up? No; the dog were in the yard.—The Constable:
The dog ran on before me.—Mr. Potter (to defendant):
You will be fined one shilling and costs, as it was out
without a muzzle.—Defendant: He was never out.

THE BUILDING TRADE STRIKES AT
BLACKBURN.

The flaggers and slaters sent round a notice some time
ago asking for an increase of wages, which will be
tantamount to an advance of about 3s a week. The
notice expires on Monday next. A deputation of the
men met a committee of the masters on Monday evening, but nothing satisfactory was arrived at. On Monday evening a conference took place between the bricklayers' labourers and twelve of the master bricklayers,
when it was decided to offer the men the advance in a
month if in the meantime they would work at the old
rate of wages.

At a meeting, last night, of the Bricklayers' Labourers'
Society the offer of the masters was considered, and it
was decided not to accept them. The masons in the
Master Builders' Association, to the number of 19, have
resolved not to move from their last offer, and to hold
no more meetings for some time. The settlement in these
strikes looks more remote than ever.

DARWEN.

THREATENING A WIFE.—At the Borough Police-court,
on Monday, Thomas Williams, carter, 22, Pole-lane, was
charged with being drunk and disorderly and assaulting
his wife.—P.C. Smith said that about 5 15 p.m. on
Saturday he found prisoner drunk in Pole-lane.—Inspector Leeming said that a complaint was lodged by the
wife that prisoner had badly ill-used her.—Mrs. Martha
Williams said on Saturday evening prisoner came to the
house drunk. As they would not let him in he broke
the back room windows, and, entering the house, used
threatening language and threw a large knife at her.
Luckily the knife missed, but then prisoner said he
would kill her, and seized a poker, with which he struck
her, inflicting serious injuries. At that moment a young
man, who was in the house at the time, grappled with
prisoner, and they fell, struggling, on the floor. The
police then came and took prisoner away.—P.C. Bailey
said prisoner deliberately struck him on the face at the
station, and caused it to swell very much.—The magistrates fined prisoner 2s 6d for being drunk and disorderly, 5s for assaulting his wife, and granted a
separation order, with an allowance of 5s a week to his
wife.

DARWEN.

A DESERTER.—At the Police-court, on Monday, George Wm. Shipstone was charged with deserting from H.M.S. Asia, at Portsmouth. He was ordered to be sent to Preston to await an escort.

A RUNAWAY HORSE.—On Monday afternoon a horse belonging to an Accrington man took fright at something in the Bolton-road, and the shafts becoming detached from the lurry the animal rushed along at a rapid pace. Two sisters named Kay, residing at Sough, were knocked down and had to be attended by Dr. J. H. Wraith. In the Circus the horse came into contact with an old man, and a woman was knocked down in Church-street.

CONSERVATIVE TEA-PARTY.—In connection with the Conservative Association, the annual tea-party took place in the Public Hall on Saturday evening. There was a fair attendance. At an entertainment which followed the tea a capital programme was gone through, the performers being Miss Young, Miss Cooper, Miss Beet, R.A.M., Messrs. Geo. Butterworth, R.A.M., Wm. Knowles, W. Woods, T. Taylor, and J. Woods (glee party). Mr. R. H. Eccles, J.P., presided, and an address was delivered by Mr. T. Fielding, of Manchester.

MR. C. P. HUNTINGTON AT TOCKHOLES.—The annual tea and meeting of the Tockholes Liberal Association was held on Saturday evening in the Silk Hall, and there was a good attendance. After tea Mr. E. Hindle presided, and the Liberal candidate delivered an address, in the course of which he spoke of the Special Commission report, and said that an election might come any day. The longer it was deferred, however, the more complete would be the Liberal victory. Alderman Shorrock, Councillor Brindle, Mr. T. Y. Nuttall, and Mr. S. Harrison were amongst those present. A musical programme was rendered at intervals.

MILL FIRE.—At mid-day on Thursday a fire occurred at Messrs. W. T. Ashton and Son's Hope Mill, Darwen. The manager (Mr. T. Rostron) who discovered the fire, immediately communicated with the borough brigade by the telephone, and in the meantime obtained assistance, and kept the flames in check by means of buckets of water. The brigade turned up promptly, and there being a good supply of water the flames were quickly subdued. The fire originated in the drawing-in room on the second storey, but the cause of it is not known. The fire applicances belonging to No. 1 Spinning Company's Mill were utilised with good effect, and the Blackburn Fire Brigade also turned up, but their services were not required. The damage, estimated at £1,000, is covered by insurance.

Sales by Auction.